PLONKERS PLAI█

Stephen █████

With Foreword by Charlie Williams

To Lond hale
with best wishes
Steve Smith

PS. See you in book 3
how do you spell
twat ??.?!!
Regards
Steve

First published in Great Britain in 1998 by

TS

Twiddlesmith Publishing Ltd
Whitton House, 11 York Road,
Beverley, East Yorkshire HU17 8DP
© Stephen D Smith, 1997

TO ALAN
WITH THANKS FOR YOUR SUPPORT
(I wear it often, even if it is a bit tight on me!)

THE AUTHOR WISHES TO THANK THE FOLLCWING:
The Rotherham Advertiser, Peter Baker Q.C., Jack Bennett, Stewart
Bradley, John Brind, Graham 'Bodger' Broom, Margaret Brown, Steve
Caddy, Carnival Films, Philip Caplan, Malcolm Carey, David Clarke,
Geoffrey Clarke, Keith Copley, Neil Crossland, Martin Dawes, BBC
Radio Derby, Dino's Restaurant Sheffield, The Doncaster Free Press,
Stuart Doughty, Beverley Doyle, Bob & Lynne Ego, The Ernest Booth
Trio, Bernard Ewart, Jon Ford, Lewis Frame, Neil Franklin, Christopher
Good, Alan Greaves, Patricia Ann Greaves (WH Smith Meadowhall),
Gary Hartley, Steven Hewitt, John Holmes, Tony & Janet Hudson, Paul
Humphries, Michael Jarvis, The Estate of Tim Johnson Deceased,
Carolann Jones (WH Smith Meadowhall), Professor Stephen Jones, Derek
Kemp, Rachel Lancashire (WH Smith Meadowhall), Peter Large, David
'Bader' Lidster, Brian Longworth, Jeni Morton, Timothy 'Tenbelly'
Norburn, Terry Nunns, Sean Page, Lionel Parker Ray Parkin, Melvyn
Prior, The Yorkshire Post, The Doncaster Free Press, Karen Price, Reilly's
Restaurant Sheffield, Paul Robinson, The Sheffield Star, Michael
Smallwood, Kate Smith, The South Yorkshire Times, Stagewear
Unlimited of Bolton-on-Dearne, Rotherham, Ann Storey, Max Tuouy,
Gordon Trousdale, Alan Twiddle, Michael Walker, Steven Wilford,
Charlie Williams, Newton Wright, and Albert.

A CIP record for this book is available from
the British Library
ISBN 1 901853 15 2 Hardback Edition
ISBN 1 901853 10 1 Paperback Edition
The right of Stephen D Smith to be identified as the author of
this work has been asserted by him in accordance with the
Copyright, Designs and Patents Act 1988

Printed in Great Britain by Redwood Books Limited,
Trowbridge, Wiltshire

CONTENTS

FOREWORD

Steve Smith is a Yorkshireman born and bred just like me. Just like me, he can tell a tale and is not afraid to tell it as it is. He can also make people laugh which is something I've been trying to do for longer than I care to remember.

The comedian and the comic writer have much in common because they both have to find their own 'voice' so that their audience sees and hears a real person.

Steve has certainly found his 'voice'. Humour dances through his books and he has created a number of seriously funny individuals. However, as in life, tears are never far from laughter and many of his most memorable characters are the victims and casualties of life.

I laughed out loud at the antics of Jack and Albert in 'Boozers Ballcocks and Bail' but cried for Mrs Daniels. I know someone just like Sean Page and have been unfortunate enough to pay for the services of a joiner who had obviously been trained by Bodger Broom.

Steve has once again drawn upon his remarkable memory to delight us with a further account of the early years of his solicitors practice in South Yorkshire. The stories, whether funny or sad, are always entertaining and the mass of characters, new and old are guaranteed to entertain to the very last page. 'Boozers Ballcocks and Bail' was a winner but 'Plonkers Plaintiffs and Pleas' is even better.

Now read on and discover that I am right.

Charlie Williams
Yorkshire
October 1997

Chapter One

ALL HE WANTS FOR XMAS IS A BOA CONSTRICTOR

"Can't it wait until after Christmas, Albert?"

It was almost 5.30pm on Christmas Eve 1982 and I was about to lock up Wilford Smith & Co. Solicitors of Rotherham when Albert Heptonstall had appeared on my doorstep.

Albert was the youngest of the nine children of Jack and Madge Heptonstall, a family which had become one of my most regular and loyal clients since I set up in business with my partner Steve Wilford. In fact, I believe that Albert was the only one I hadn't represented in court but, as he was only fourteen, there was plenty of time for him to follow in the family tradition. I had already discovered that he had a fascination for police cars when he had managed to break into a police compound, get into a police car and play with the short wave radio. His handiwork resulted in the complete breakdown of all the mobile police radios in the Rotherham area.

In the past, Albert had only ever come to the office with his father but this time he was alone and the usual, omnipresent Heptonstall grin had disappeared. I was to find out that this wasn't all that had disappeared.

As Albert began to speak, I heard the strains of "Silent night, Holy night" emanating from the tannoy system in the church across the way. The setting could have been perfect: Christmas carols, a lighted Christmas tree, large flakes of snow and Albert!

"You see Steve, it's like this...you'll never believe it!"

"Go on then Albert, I'm all ears.

1

"We've lost Elliott," said Albert ruefully. "We've lost him, he's gone......gone." With that the usually happy-go-lucky Albert bowed his head as if struck by some terrible malady.

My mind raced through the names of Jack's children as I tried to put a face to the one who was missing:

Horace, Boris, Morris and Venn, Cloris, Doris, Lorris and Tyrone; but no Elliott. Who the hell was Elliott? I could stand the suspense no longer.

"Albert?" I ventured carefully.

"Argh," said Albert.

"Who is Elliott?" I asked, fearing that some secret illegitimate child had been lost forever in the abyss known as Canklow a sub district of Rotherham.

"It's me boa," said Albert.

"It's your what?" I asked somewhat confused.

"Me boa," said Albert.

I did not wish to show my ignorance, but there seemed no option.

"What's a boa?" I asked.

Albert paused for a moment, as if in a trance, and then said,

"It's a constricting non-venomous reptile which crushes its prey by compression. The initial attack is remarkably quick and is usually made with the mouth open."

At this point Albert demonstrated by forcing his mouth as wide open as possible. He then continued.

"A coil is simultaneously thrown around the victim and is then strengthened by the other coils."

I was speechless and I felt that my mouth had dropped open further than any boa constrictors jaws possibly could. How on earth was Albert able to speak so fluently and knowledgeably on such a subject? He was the first to speak, taking my silence and surprised expression as a signal for further explanation.

2

"It's a snake, a bloody big un' an' all, all five foot of 'im. Some git 'as pinched 'im. The thieving bastard." Albert finished and I finally understood.

The little fellow was distraught and I realised poor old Albert was most put out.

I tried to cheer him up by asking him about Elliott.

"Where is the snake from Albert?"

Noting my interest, Albert seemed to brighten a little.

"He's from where the Indians come from in Asia. Tha knows Indians dunt tha?......Ghandi, Nehru.........Sitting bull, Geronimo, tha knows?"

"Oh yes, of course," I replied, thoughtfully. I had difficulty with Albert's geography, In fact I had difficulty with just about everything Albert said, but I think he meant well.

"How're your mum and dad then Albert?" I asked, trying to change the subject completely.

"Dad's alreight, but mother's upset."

"Why's that Albert?" I asked, fearing that I was about to open a can of worms.

"Th'al niver believe this either, but we wa' burgled yisterdey."

"Never", I said in astonishment.

"Aye", said Albert, "We were all art and someone must have been watching t' ouse 'cos they brock into me dad's shed and 'ad some of 'is tools away. They got inta kitchin an' all, and that's what really upset me mother."

"Why was that Albert?" I enquired.

"Well the dirty bastards did sommat."

"What was that Albert?" I asked, dreading the answer.

"Well me mother 'ad a big pot a stew ont' cooker like, ready to cook for tea. It must 'ave been some bugger wi' a grudge 'cos the dirty bastard did 'is business int' pot."

3

I was horrified, even though I had come across defendants who had behaved in such a disgusting manner on a number of occasions.

"It reight upset me mother that did."

"I can imagine Albert, it's terrible."

"Aye", said Albert. "She was that upset tha knows, because she 'ad to chuck 'alf of it away."

It was time to change the subject yet again.

"What the bloody hell are you doing with a five foot boa constrictor in the first place Albert?"

"Fuck all now," replied Albert in his eloquent way. "'ees gone, nicked, pinched, leafed, swiped, knocked off...."

Before Albert could think of further synonyms for the word stolen, I interrupted him.

"How do you know he's been pinched," I asked, "Maybe he just slithered off."

"'e was in transit," said Albert.

Albert always phrased his replies in such a way that he kept the listener interested, a trait he had picked up from his father. It was almost as if he was sharing a secret with you.

"In transit? From where and to where, may I ask?" I did ask.

"No. 'e was in a Transit van!"

"Oh! So where is the van now?" I enquired cautiously.

"That's the point," Albert whispered, "It's gone an' all."

"Gone an' all," I replied.

"Argh, nicked, pinched, leafed........."

"Yes." I said, interrupting his flow, "I understand: And Elliott?"

We both spoke simultaneously:

"Ee's in the van!"

4

"Now let me see if I have got this right," I said. "You have an extremely large snake and you keep him in your father's van?"

"No," said Albert correcting me. "Our Morris's van. You see, me father wain't let him int' house."

"Who?" I asked, "Morris?"

"Neow, Elliott. Me father wain't let Elliott int' house."

"Why not?" I queried.

"Cos o' shit," said Albert bluntly.

"What shit?" I asked, beginning to lose patience.

"Elliott's. Me father dun't like snake shit int' house."

"I can understand that" I countered as I started to imagine just what boa constrictor excrement might look like.

"Not only that," continued Albert, "'ee's a bit friendly."

"Who is, your father?"

"Neow, Elliott," said Albert.

"Oh, sorry Albert, I wasn't quite following you."

"Tha sees, we keep 'im int' green'ouse where its warm, because ee dun't like cold. If we dun't ger'im back quick 'eel dee." Albert was obviously getting upset thinking about his beloved pet, cold and alone on Christmas Eve.

I glanced out of the window to see the Christmas Tree with its fairy lights on branches weighed down with snow. My thoughts then returned to Albert, who was clearly concerned enough to walk the three miles from home to my office in his search for his bloody snake. I couldn't help thinking that there were plenty of snakes in Rotherham but they were not all members of the reptile family.

"What do you feed him on?" I asked.

"Nowt now," said Albert sulkily.

"OK. What about before he was stolen?" I asked.

"Oh then?" said Albert, "He would eat the odd rat or mouse or even some'at bigger."

5

"And how often did you have to feed him?" I asked.

"Ivery day," said Albert, "If you don't 'ee gets a bit restless."

"I can imagine." I replied.

"Argh, and that's when ee gets a bit friendly".

"Friendly!?" I asked.

"Arghh, friendly," said Albert.   "Ee likes to get friendly round thee neck."

"And then what does he do?" I asked pointedly.

"Squeeeezes." said Albert, making a gurgling noise as if he was being strangled.

"How long have you had Elliott?" I asked.

"About six months now," said Albert, "I swapped him for three koi carp, a whippet, and some spare parts off me dad's Skoda.   It was a good deal really because the Skoda's knackered and the whippet were in't club, but it's gone to a reight good 'ome with a bloke who breeds them on a farm."

"So he's got a good deal then hasn't he? If he's got a whippet that's going to have pups?"

"Ah, 'ee 'as until it 'as em."

"What do you mean by that?" I asked.

"Because I think the father were a sheep dog".

"What was Elliott doing in the van?" I asked.

"'Ee was in his golf bag where 'ee lives.   It's a big golf bag and it opens at t'side in-stead o' top and it's got, like, cushion inside to keep him warm.   He sleeps a lot, but he's reight affectionate."

"Yes, I'm sure he is, particularly if he gets you round the neck.   But aren't these type of snakes dangerous Albert?" I asked.

"Neow, tha's just got to mek sure it dun't get thee round t'neck, cos it'll gi thee a reight 'eadache".

A thought suddenly occurred to me that whoever stole the transit van was driving around with a potentially lethal snake on board.   Even if I wasn't worried about the thief's well-being, I certainly should be bothered about other road users. If the snake should get friendly while the driver was at the wheel, the consequences could be tragic.   Not only that, Albert wanted his snake back and I would think that Morris wanted his van.

I began taking notes.

"What else was there in the van apart from the snake in the golf bag?" I asked.

"There's an electric pump for a garden pond."

"Yes" I replied, jotting it down as Albert continued.

"Some spanners."

"Yes, spanners," I repeated.

"There's like a big plastic doll...."

"A big plastic what?" I asked.

"Doll", said Albert, "One of them that tha blows up."

I paused for a minute to consider what I was to write before repeating Albert's words:

"Large...blow...up...doll.   Who does that belong to?" I asked.

"Our Morris borrowed it from Boris."

"Oh", I said, knowing that to ask any more would be potentially dangerous.

"Anything else?"

"Argh", said Albert, "There is."

"Well what?" I asked.

"Twenty thousand Benson and Hedges," Albert announced with a casual air.

"And where did they come from?" I asked.

"They're mi dad's" said Albert, "And 'ee dunt know the've gone yit.   'e likes a smoke tha knows".

I decided not to push the point for fear of what Albert might tell me and I decided not to complete my inventory. I looked Albert in the eye and asked him what he proposed to do.

"The thieving bastard will ger it when me dad finds art." Albert said this at the same time as pulling a gruesome face and thumping his right fist into the palm of his left hand.

"I've no doubt Albert, no doubt whatsoever. But that doesn't help the situation at the moment, does it?"

"What do I do then Steve?" asked Albert. "After all, it's Christmas and I've got Elliott two rats for his Christmas present."

I suggested that the theft should be reported to the Police.

"Oh I can't do that", said Albert, "Me dad'll niver wear that".

"Fine, then I will report it," I replied. Albert was even less enthusiastic about that suggestion. After all, he was the client and if he didn't wish to report it there was nothing that I could do to force him. However, I reiterated my concerns for other road users and Albert saw the point.

After a long discussion, we decided that he would put an advertisement in the local paper under "Lost and Found" in the hope that the thief or his associates might see it and feel disposed to hand back the stolen goods.

I very much doubted that this would achieve anything, but at least we were doing something and, after all, it was Christmas Eve and the sooner we reached a decision, the sooner I would get home.

"Steve, would you write the advert for me?"

"Of course I will. I will do it now and you can add anything to it that you feel might be appropriate," I said.

I took a piece of paper from the reception desk and wrote: "LOST OR STOLEN, ONE BOA CONSTRICTOR. A FORD TRANSIT VAN WAS TAKEN ON 23RD DECEMBER AND IT CONTAINED A VERY

DANGEROUS SNAKE WHICH SHOULD BE RETURNED TO ITS OWNER IMMEDIATELY. PLEASE TELEPHONE: 382121 AND ASK FOR ALBERT".

I handed the note to Albert who felt he should have something to offer in return.

"Tha dunt want any bottles of whisky for Christmas does tha Steve?"

"No thank you Albert, I'm trying to give it up" I said, avoiding the certain prospect of handling stolen goods.

As we finished our business, Albert got up from the chair and held out his hand for me to shake. I did so in the certain knowledge that I was looking at a lad whose destiny was to become a professional thief. Yet I couldn't help liking the little bugger. Jack, his father, had never claimed benefit, but had lived a life of dishonesty, which his children accepted as being part of a normal life style. After all, I don't suppose Albert's behaviour was all his own fault. He had never been corrected or given proper direction, although he had been taught a certain moral code. He was respectful to the elderly and, like his father, would never consider defiling anyone's home by burgling it. However, as Jack used to say, the "commercials" were fair game.

As Albert reached the door he looked back at me with such intensity that I could not help but feel sorry for him. Albert was just a little boy who had lost his favourite pet.

"I will get 'im back, waint a?"

"I hope so," I replied, "I really do hope so."

"Well, Merry Christmas then," Albert said, trying to smile.

"Yes, Merry Christmas Albert, and a Happy New Year."

As I stood at the door watching Albert trudging through the slushy snow, I felt the cold wind blowing flecks of snow onto my face. I shivered and realised that Albert wasn't dressed for a long walk home on such a cold and wet evening.

I called him back, grabbing my coat and briefcase. I tried to put my arm into the sleeve but I noticed that some bright spark had sellotaped a balloon inside it and attached a note which read: "This is a balloon not a hump."

I immediately recognised Pagey's handwriting.

I gave Albert the balloon and walked over to the taxi rank with him. There were two taxis waiting and I went over to the first one and asked the driver to deliver Albert to his front door. As I paid the fare, Albert jumped into the back and began waving to me as the taxi pulled off. The Heptonstall grin was back on his face as the thought of arriving home in a taxi made him forget Elliott for a little while at least.

I moved back, smiling until 'my' taxi, the second one in the rank flew past me at speed, sending a tidal wave of slush breaking over me. I swore and shook my fist at the disappearing taxi but then, as my ears cleared of the slush, I heard the strains of 'God rest ye merry gentlemen' coming from the church and I immediately felt guilty. It was Christmas and by the time the next taxi arrived I was cold and wet but happy, looking forward to Christmas.

Chapter Two

TANK MAKES A FASHION STATEMENT & PAGEY LIVES TO TELL THE TALE

I arrived home slightly damp and very late.

We were on our way to our Christmas Eve dinner with the Great Jarvis and Tenbelly Norburn and their partners, a tradition which continues to this day.

Christmas was over when the phone rang early on Boxing Day. It was the local police station ringing to inform me that there was to be special Boxing Day court and my services had been requested by the infamous Eric Dobkin, alcoholic and reveller supreme.

He was demanding my presence at the local cells to represent him that morning, but more importantly he wanted a packet of Benson and Hedges as he had been without smokes throughout the night.

On Christmas night Eric had seen fit to climb up the large Christmas tree which is a feature of the town centre decorations. Having got to the top, he was unable to get back down and eventually his weight was such that the tree began to topple over, causing him to fall, and to land in the nearby fountain. This greatly entertained the gathered throng, but unfortunately, amongst the revellers were officers of the South Yorkshire Police who were not as amused and arrested him for breach of the peace and causing criminal damage.

And so, I set off for the special lock-up court. It was particularly inconvenient, as one of my favourite films 'The Prisoner of Zenda' starring Ronald Coleman was on television. Nevertheless, duty called and off I went to see Eric and two other clients who had been arrested for similar offences.

11

Eric complained that the police had refused to release him, causing him to miss Christmas night with his family. He wanted to make a formal complaint because he said the police had been visiting his cell in the early hours singing Christmas carols and deliberately keeping him awake. I told him not to bother with the complaint and to concentrate on trying to get bail but, as ever, Eric did not agree with the advice being given to him. I had been unable to get him any cigarettes but had found an old Christmas cigar still in its tube which I passed over to him. He smoked it furiously in the small interview room, causing me to cough repeatedly.

"Bad cough that," said Eric.

"Yes, it's the cigar smoke in such a small confined space that is irritating my throat and larynx to the point that it is forcing me to cough," said I, hoping that he might get the point and put it out.

"That's a bugger that," said Eric continuing to puff away.

I managed to agree bail for all my clients, but Eric was given a condition not to enter licensed premises. This did not meet with his complete approval.

"What am I going to do about going out for a drink?" said Eric. "They can't stop me from drinking in the house, can they?"

"No, so drink in the house then," came my reply.

"Neow, I'm not having that, bloody hell it's Christmas for Christ's sake."

I found his biblical utterances quite interesting, if not rather poignant, but the magistrates' had made their decision and for Eric the boozers were out of bounds whether he liked it or not. The case was adjourned until the New Year and I told him that if he got arrested on New Year's Eve, there would be no way that I would turn out to help him.

As I got home, Ronald Coleman was riding his horse into the sunset, being waved off by C Aubury Smith and David Niven. In the certain knowledge that the police would be bothering me again, I began to think that life would be easier if I left the legal profession and opened a tobacconist shop.

The following day, an advertisement in the local paper caught my eye. Under 'Lost and Found', I read:

NICKED WITH TRANSIT VAN

ONE BOA CONSTRICTOR (A SNAKE)

THERE IS A REWARD FOR THIS VAN AND CONTENTS

AND THE BOA WHICH WERE STOLEN ON THE 23rd

DECEMBER

REWARD OFFERED

CAUTION WITH SNAKE IF IT GETS FRIENDLY -

PLEASE KEEP AWAY FROM NECK. IT ANSWERS TO

THE NAME ELLIOTT

PLEASE RING JACK OR ALBERT

ON ROTHERHAM: 382121

OR

WILFORD SMITH ON ROTHERHAM: 828044

The advert was not quite as I had drafted it, and I certainly couldn't remember offering our office as a contact point. As I knew the paper would have already been circulated to over 30,000 homes, I waited with baited breath to see what calls might come our way.

One caller wanted details of the thief so that he could 'kill him'. Another telephoned to say that he could give us no information at all and a third offered to buy the snake if we found it. The other callers were referred to Albert, who wallowed in the waves of sympathy he received from pet-lovers throughout South Yorkshire. The one thing we didn't receive was any information on the whereabouts of Elliott.

On New Years Eve, we were to close the office at noon and in the morning I decided to clear my desk and dictate some work. Unfortunately at 9.15a.m. I received a telephone call requesting my attendance at the cells. I was asked to represent a local car thief who had committed offences while already subject to bail. When defendants are released on bail they are warned that if they offend again a remand in custody is the likely result.

Gerald David Robert Gutherie Allison, commonly known as 'Tank' was a young lad about twenty years old who had been brought up on a local housing estate where crime was rife. He had spent the greatest part of his short adult life in one custodial setting after another. Institutional life was grim, but Tank had enlivened the day to day drudgery of it all by learning essential skills such as how to remove lead from roofs, how to hot wire cars and how to break windows silently. This particular skill involved brown paper and a specific brand of treacle.

The most popular avenue of recreation for the criminally minded was car crime, which meant that they either stole cars or took their contents. Tank was a master craftsman and it was said that he could beat any of the sophisticated electronic locking systems.

He came into the small interview room in the call area and I greeted him enthusiastically.

"Good morning Mr Gutherie and to what do we owe this pleasure? Don't tell me it's pinching cars."

"Arh Mr Smith, it is aye, but they've got me on these bang to rights, I've got four charges and fifteen TIC's and don't tell me that I'm up shit creek for bail?"

Tank's forte was Ford motor vehicles and true to form his four charges involved Cortinas which he described as 'easy meat'. I had not paid too much attention to the schedule of offences

14

to be 'taken into consideration', save to note that they were also Fords which Tank had freely admitted to stealing.

"Correct in all particulars Mr Gutherie," I said, "and by the way, I love the suit."

Tank was wearing the police issue jump suit which is made out of a white paper-like material which covers the entire body including the feet and fastens with a zipper at the neck. The police issue this snazy item when they take a defendant's clothing for forensic tests.

Tank had been accused of a burglary during which a window had been damaged and threads from a jumper had been found on a jagged piece of glass. Tank's clothing had been taken to see if the fibres found on the glass would match those from his jumper.

Tank had denied the burglary and the tests were to be carried out in an attempt to prove that he was guilty. The prosecution wished to remand Tank in custody because he had broken his bail and Tank was most put out.

It was unfortunate that he had not put his considerable skills to use in a work capacity, for without doubt he would have been a success. So many of the young criminals of today are extremely bright and could find work if they wanted to. To say that unemployment causes crime is not always true because many youths commit crime just for the 'buzz', and we have to face the fact that some are simply dishonest by nature.

Young Gutherie was a peculiar character, almost as wide as he was tall, standing at five foot, six inches but weighing eighteen stones. He once explained his obesity by telling me that it was achieved by being 'a pig'. He was generally of an unkempt appearance and his personal hygiene left a great deal to be desired However, he was pleasant enough and easy to deal with.

We joked about his dress sense and I offered to use my influence with the police to enable him to keep the paper jump suit, as I thought it might become all the rage in Rotherham as a fashion statement. I then proceeded to consider his charges. I told him that a bail application was pointless but he insisted and as it was his right, we sat together for a moment trying to think of how to word the application.

It was quite warm in the small interview area and before leaving for court Tank decided to unzip the top of the jump suit. This revealed his neck complete with gold medallion. As I got up I couldn't help but notice some strange marks which looked like tyre treads around Tank's neck. As we walked up to the court room, I looked more closely and noticed that the row of marks continued down the full length of his neck. My view then became obscured as we walked up the spiral staircase to the court. I made the bail application as best I could but, not surprisingly, the magistrates were against me and remanded Tank in custody to the local cells for three days so that enquiries could be made into the burglary.

With my court business over for the day, I returned to the office to collect any messages and to check the post. When I went into my room I found what appeared to be a large golf bag at the side of my desk. It had a message attached to it which read:

"On seeing the advert in the paper, we realised this might be what you are looking for. Please return it to it's owner."

There was no name or address, just the bag. I stood for a while gazing at it before moving nearer. I peered in cautiously but found, very much to my surprise, that the side zip was open and the bag was empty.

I decided that I would go in search of a snake and in the corridor I saw Jack Bennett.

"Hello Steve, are you looking for something?"

"Yes," I replied, "I'm looking for a snake."

"Oh, he's in Wilf's room," said Jack. "You do mean Sean Page don't you?"

"No," I said, "Not that sort of snake, but thank you anyway," and I continued my search.

When I reached the waiting room, I was so intent upon finding my quarry that I did not immediately notice a number of people sitting down. Realising that my behaviour might seem strange I announced,

"Excuse me, I'm sorry to bother you, but I'm looking for a snake." Immediately grasping the apparent absurdity of what I said, I laughed, and fortunately so did they.

I went to our receptionist.

"Tracey," I shouted, "Was this bag empty when it was brought in?"

"I don't know," said Tracey, "I didn't look inside, someone just left it on the desk. I didn't see who'd brought it. When I took it into your room it was quite heavy."

"Do me a favour. Just pick the bag up now and tell me if it weights the same," I asked. Exercising great caution, Tracey picked up the bag.

"Oh no," she said, "It was much heavier that this."

"Thanks very much," I said as I continued the search.

"Tracey," I shouted, "You haven't seen anything that looks rather greasy, about five feet in length have you?"

"Yes," she said, "I have."

I breathed a sigh of relief. "Where is it?" I asked.

"It's in Wilf's room, one of Pagey's mates, he's come to see Wilf about some conveyancing."

"I didn't mean a human being," I said, "I meant something else of about five feet in length that looks rather greasy."

"Do you mean a client?"

17

"No, I mean a constricting non-venomous reptile which crushes its prey by compression."

"What are you talking about?" asked Tracey.

"Never mind," I said, not wanting to alarm her any more. I picked up the telephone and rang a number which had become quite familiar to me.

"Yeh," came the answer.

"Is that Albert?" I asked.

"Yeh," came the answer.

"It's Steve Smith here."

"Yeh."

"I take it you're still looking for the snake?"

"Yeh."

"May I ask you about the golf bag? It wouldn't happen to be red with a brass zip would it?"

"Yeh," came the answer.

"And would it have a gold coloured strap at the side?"

"Yeh, you haven't found it?" asked Albert, his voice raised in hope.

"Yeh," I replied.

"Reight," said Albert, "I'm on me way, me brother will run me in."

With that I put the telephone down, still looking about me rather apprehensively.

Not understanding the habits of a boa constrictor, I wasn't entirely sure where to look, but Elliott had quite clearly gone for a slither somewhere around my office. I felt I had to try to find him before he frightened some unsuspecting person to death, particularly because I suspected my insurance would not cover such an eventuality.

As I left my room I heard a loud cry from Wilf's office.

"What the fucking hell is that!!!??"

I recognised the voice. I went in to find Pagey jumping up and down as though he was on fire while trying to wrench a boa constrictor called Elliott from his left arm.

"Get the fucking thing off," shouted Pagey.

I dissolved into laughter and as laughter is incredibly infections, particularly if you are not on the receiving end, it wasn't long before Wilf and Pagey's five foot tall greasy friend had joined in. Pagey wasn't laughing. He was fighting to keep Elliott from moving up his arm towards his neck.

"He's only trying to be friendly," I said, doubled up with laughter. All Pagey could say was, "Get him off, get him off", and one or two expletives which only made things worse. Pagey was not normally given to bad language, but Elliott had obviously upset him.

"Oh look at him, he like's you," I announced.

"Get it off, get if off," cried Pagey, as sweat began pouring from his brow.

Although I realised that I hadn't any idea at all of how to handle the snake, it didn't seem to matter. Wilf and I guffawed with glee and Pagey's friend soon joined in. Pagey was not impressed,

"You bastards!" said a much irritated Page. "Get the fucking thing off."

Wilf was less than happy about getting involved.

"I'm not touching it, I hate snakes," he announced with a chuckle.

Pagey's friend was convulsed with laughter and could do nothing, and unfortunately for the hapless Page I did not feel disposed to get involved either.

I remembered that Jack Bennett had been a serving soldier in Burma and would therefore know all about snakes and how to deal with them. I called him, but to little benefit. He had been more frightened of the snakes than he had been of the Japanese.

"I couldn't go near those bloody things, they haunted my life out in Burma, they were everywhere, in the rooms, under the bed and even in the latrines. You couldn't sit down to mind your own business without worrying."

"Get it off," repeated Pagey as Elliott moved further towards his shoulder. Pagey's shouted orders had changed to quiet pleadings for help.

Jack continued rather casually,

"Can't go near them," he continued, "Horrible bloody things, I remember once in Rangoon a medical orderly......" Before Jack could speak further Page interrupted,

"Never mind the bleeding history lesson Jack, get it off please." Jack would have none of it.

"Sorry Pagey," he said, "I know what these buggers can do, I'm off."

Pagey's pal was now on the floor, clutching his stomach, aching with laughing. Pagey cursed the retreating Jack as Elliott continued his journey along Pagey's arm.

"Get the sodding thing off," said Pagey. "Hit it with something or cut it's head off, but do something."

Wilf and I considered the situation for a moment or two and realised that if we were to interfere the snake might not like it and set out for us. On the other hand, Elliott may well choke Pagey and we would obviously feel in someway responsible. The choice was clear: We decided to leave Pagey to his fate.

"Don't leave me with this fucking thing you bastards, get it off."

I could think of nothing to say or do, save for,

"Here Elliott, here boy, here Elliott, come on lad, good boy."

Pagey looked at me in disgust,

"You bloody idiot. GET...IT...OFF...ME."

20

Pagey was beginning to panic, which was more than could be said for his mate who was still on the floor trying to conceal a rather damp patch around the crotch of his trousers. By this time Elliott's face was almost in line with Pagey's neck.

"Oh Christ," said Pagey, "It's going to kill me, it's going to kill me."

"Give him a hand," I said to Wilf. "Help him for God's sake."

Wilf looked at me in astonishment.

"You help him, I hate snakes."

"Bugger that for a game of soldiers," I said. "I'm not getting involved in that, the owner's on his way, he should be here in a few minutes."

"Bloody marvellous that," said Pagey, "The bastard will have killed me by then. Just cut it's head off or something."

"With what?" I asked.

"What about a knife?" said Pagey. "Just hit the bastard or something."

None of us made any attempt to go near Elliott, but we all noticed that Pagey's hand had begun to turn blue. Elliott was turning on the pressure.

"Don't worry Pagey, it's not poisonous," I said rather weakly.

Pagey looked at me in disgust.

"No, you bastard, it will have crushed me to death before it gets to poison me. That is a great relief I can assure you."

I decided that I had to intervene, as Pagey was about to faint.

"Get hold it it's head," I said to Wilf.

"Fuck off," said Wilford, "You get hold of it's head!"

Alright, you get hold of it's tail then," I asked.

"Fuck off," replied Wilford. "I'm not touching it. It'll turn on me."

"When you've finished arguing," said Pagey, "Would someone please save my life?"

At that very second fortunately for Pagey, Albert walked in and took charge. He went over to Pagey and said "Try not to panic. You are upsetting him."

"I'm upsetting him?" spluttered Pagey incredulously, "I'm upsetting him?" What the hell do you think he's doing to me? Ouch."

Albert weaved his magic spell and within a few seconds he had got the loving Elliott in his arms and around his waist.

"He's only being friendly," said Albert to Pagey , "he obviously likes you."

"Yes and I like him in much the same way I adore piles and a brain haemorrhage. That bloody thing ought to be put down."

"Neh geoar," said Albert. "There's 'nowt wrong with 'im 'e's as soft as they come."

"He's a nightmare," said Pagey beginning to recover. "Just look at all it's crap on my arm," he moaned as he noticed streams of a gooey type liquid along his sleeve.

"You see, that proves he likes you," said Albert.

"Why is that?" said Pagey.

"That's snake shit. They won't do it unless they are comfortable."

Pagey pointed to his own bottom and said, "Yes, and that's human shit caused by being frightened to death by a snake. You ought to have a licence for that thing."

Unlike the rest of us, Pagey would not see the funny side of things, but then we had not been the object of a snake's affection.

Albert asked who had returned the bag, but we were unable to tell him.

"I don't suppose they've left the twenty thousand fags?" said Albert.

"No I don't suppose they have," I said, "But there it is."

22

We all saw the funny side of things, but for once Pagey did not although his 5' tall greasy friend more than made up for it in what was perhaps his best afternoon out ever.

Albert, was delighted. He had been reunited with his friend Elliott and could not have been happier. I went to the door with Albert and the Heptonstall grin was back again, wider than ever.

As he walked across the courtyard to catch the bus home, I saw him stop to speak to one of his friends, who shrieked in horror when he peered into the bag. Albert laughed and ran for his bus.

We closed the office at 1pm and set off to the Brecon for a bar meal and some liquid refreshment.

We were soon joined by Bodger and Jarvis.

I decided to get the first round. Wilf and I were on double gins and Jarvis a large brandy, Bodger had a pint of lager while I ordered a 'snake bite' for Pagey.

Within an hour, Pagey had seen the funny side of things and began to relate his story as though it had all been a huge joke set up by himself. He turned to a stranger who appeared at the bar and pointed to the staining on his suit sleeve.

"You'll never guess what these marks are," said Pagey.

"No," said the curious guest. "What are they?"

"Snake shit," said Pagey, and with that he picked up his glass and joined us at a table.

"Do you know that chap?" I asked.

"No," said Pagey, "Never seen him before in my life."

Three days later, my client Tank reappeared before the magistrates having been cleared of burglary as the forensic science laboratory could find nothing to incriminate him.

However, he had admitted, a number of other offences, involving motor vehicles, one of which was the theft of a Transit van. There would be no reprieve in the case.

When I visited him in the cells he was resigned to his fate. We prepared what we could by way of mitigation and I was impressed with his realistic and philosophical view as to his fate.

It is always much easier when defendants take advice, because you can do a much better job for them.

With Tank accepting the inevitable, I was able to be realistic with the bench and keep the sentence down to a minimum. Courts prefer defendants who are realistic.

As we prepared to start the case in court number 1, I noticed something rolled up on the seat in the dock next to Tank. I realised that it was the white paper jump suit in which Tank had lived for the past three days while his clothes were checked,

"They let you keep it then Tank?" I asked.

"Ah, it's reight comfortable tha knows, and I think it could set a trend in Rotherham. Everybody and their grandmothers will want one of these when they see me out in it."

"I have no doubt about that Tank," I said. "By the way, there was one thing I wanted to ask you before I go."

"Ask away," said Tank. "It looks like I'll be here for a while."

"Those marks on your neck, I just wondered how you got them?"

Tank laughed and shrugged his shoulders.

"Steve," he said in quiet reflection, "I'll tell you but you'll never believe it!"

And do you know...........he was wrong.

Chapter Three

MRS. MOTT'S KIDS

By the end of February 1983 Wilford Smith & Co. were the fastest growing firm of solicitors in the area.   Despite the deepening recession and record unemployment, we were thriving and on the point of taking on two extra members of staff to cope with the ever increasing work load.   Wilf and I were enjoying life to the full with the rewards that the successful business were giving us.   We were inseparable. We were the best of friends and business partners in pursuit of a dream of financial security and independence.   We had everything we could wish for.   Indeed we felt we were the luckiest men alive.

We also had the 'Dream Team', a group of friends who would do anything to help each other.

Wilf and I could count upon the good offices of our great friend and confidante Michael Jarvis.   He looked after the accounts and did his best to look after us as we plundered our way through our financial reserves.

Lewis Frame, the 'Mad Scotsman' from the Leeds Permanent Building Society helped us with conveyancing as did Timbo Johnson from the Bradford and Bingley and his best mate Fred from the Eagle Star.   Keith Copley, the principal clerk from the magistrates clerk's office was a bar room pal with whom I shared many a joke in the court rooms of Rotherham where I spent most of my working day.

Our odd-job man supreme, Bodger Broom, could be trusted to appear whenever his services were required and there was always Sean Page who would just appear.   Pagey was a very regular visitor who with his schizophrenic humour would drive us to the point of distraction, when we would be forced to throw him out.

Some of the best times we had were when the gang got together for our monthly soirees. These were regularly attended by two other good friends, Tenbelly Norburn and Chris Good.

One such evening had been planned for early March, when, about a week before, as I was browsing through the increasing amount of junk mail that came through the door each day, I spotted an impressively embossed invitation. It was a request for me to attend a variety show at the Rotherham Civic Theatre.

The programme included a number of entertainers who had been plugging away at their trade for many years in the micawberistic belief that something would 'turn up'.

One name that I recognised was that of Rik Romola, a magician, who's assistant, Mitch, was a bad tempered chimpanzee. Rik had been in showbusiness for over twenty years and had long since given up any idea of hitting the 'big time'. Drink had become his escape from the real world of seedy clubs and tatty bed-sits. He was dissatisfied and disillusioned and it seemed his attitude had rubbed off on Mitch. The chimp was ill-mannered and aggressive and any acts that had worked the same circuit as Rik learnt quickly to keep a safe distance between themselves and his nasty assistant. The only reason Rik got work was that he was cheap and one of a dwindling number of novelty acts that could fill a gap between a singer and a comedian.

As the invitation promised 'a night to remember', I decided to get in touch with the gang and suggest we start our evening out a little earlier at the Civic Theatre. Everyone agreed and so I rang Bob Ego at Reilly's Restaurant, Crosspool, Sheffield and put back our table booking by an hour.

Just before 5.00pm Sean Marmaduke Rufus Page, insurance broker extraordinaire and all round good egg rang me.

"Hello old chap, what's to do?" asked Pagey with just a hint of inebriation.

"I'm not bad Sean, how are you?"

"Knackered dear boy. I've had to work this morning. Good grief, whatever next?"

"Full time, old chap?" I suggested.

"Steady on dear boy, steady on. Look, I hear that you're on the razzle tonight?"

"Yes," I replied cautiously. "What about it?"

"Thought I might join you old chap," ventured Pagey.

"Why not?" I said, "There's Jarvis, Goody, Norburn, Wilf, Walker, Bodger and me but we're all going to the Civic Theatre first to watch the cabaret.

"Oh, well done," enthused Pagey, "I've got a pal on the show. Well the thing is he was a pal. We were at school together you know and I met up with him again at the old boys reunion last year. You remember the one where I had that little misunderstanding with the High Court judge over the sleeping arrangements?"

"Yes Sean, I remember." I said, thinking that it was a little more that a 'little misunderstanding."

"Well," Sean continued, "Max went into showbusiness after he left school. With a name like Crapper, I expected he would have used a stage name but he didn't and when I saw a poster in the Town Hall announcing his appearance, I thought I should give my support for the sake of the old school. So if you are going to be there, let's meet up and I'll take you and the gang backstage to meet old Max. We'll have a drink with him because he can't go in front of an audience unless he's pissed. By the way Stephen my good man, did I ever tell you the story of Max and the laxative chocolate?"

27

"Sorry Sean, I've got to go but you can tell me tonight. See you at the theatre at 7.00pm O.K?" I said.

"Topping idea Old Bean. See you there." And with that Sean hung up.

It was a recipe for disaster, the stage, alcohol and Page. I should have known better but it sounded like a good idea at the time.

Page was late and as the curtain was going up just after 7.30pm, I heard a commotion at the end of the row where we were sitting. Looking towards the noise, I saw Pagey staggering along the line of seats excusing himself as he stood on people's feet and fell onto a number of laps as he went.

"Sorry old darling………excuse me………I say that's a nice hat….what a large nut you must have."

Page was then interrupted by another member of the audience.

"Would you mind sitting down and being quiet."

"Certainamout Madame pardoney moi. By the way, where did you get that ice cream?" asked Page.

"Sit down!!" shouted the aggrieved guest.

Page finally joined our group stealing Norburns ice-cream in the process. By this time the first act, a dancer, had finished without me seeing a single step.

At the interval Page took us backstage as promised.

On the way Page explained that when he was at school he found a bar of laxative chocolate in matron's room. He put it in his pocket unsure of what he would do with it but minutes later he heard a prefect shout at a boy who was running down the school corridor.

"Stop running Crapper, you little shit!" he bellowed after the boy who had forgotten one of the numerous school rules.

That was it! Crapper was the perfect victim for laxative chocolate. So Page set about planning a wonderful ruse.

Before he could tell us what he did all those years ago, we were backstage and had all been introduced to Max. Max was worried. He was to be the last act of the evening and as a comedian his job was to send the audience home with smiles on their faces. He knew he was not a good comic because he was too nervous and when he had first spotted Page approaching him, his expression changed from one of serious apprehension to one of blind terror. He made some excuse and left us to get our own drinks.

Page then took something out of his pocket. He smiled as he showed us the inoffensive looking bar of dark chocolate. He'd 'borrowed' it from his mum who worked in a nursing home.

"Fancy a piece?" he asked.

"No thanks," said Jarvis, "Try Norburn, his need is greater than mine."

"Put it away Sean?" I said, "That could do some damage."

"Certainly could," said Page. "We'll have to try it out on someone later."

Page has a cruel sense of humour, but he is great company even if he is completely mad.

Just then Rik came in with his assistant, Mitch, on his shoulder. The chimp was spitting at people as they walked past but it made the mistake of its short life when it tugged one of Pagey's ears.

"I say, steady on," said Page to Rik, "That could do some damage if you're not careful!"

"It was your own fault," said Rik, "You shouldn't have upset him."

"Upset him, there ought to be a muzzle on that," said Page as the nasty creature pulled at his hair.

"Ger off!" said Page. "That bloody thing could be carrying disease."

"Well if he is he will have caught it off you," said Rik aggressively.

Rik then moved off but not before Mitch pulled a wax grape from the Lady Mayoress's hat. As if he knew that Pagey had been complaining about him, he took careful aim and threw the grape, hitting Pagey at the back of the head.

Little did Mitch know it, but at that moment war had been declared.

As Rik went to the bar for yet another drink, Mitch sat on a chair near to our group. Norburn held out his hand towards Mitch and the chimp immediately bit it. Pagey took the chocolate out of his pocket, looked at it and then looked at the chimp. The chimp looked at the piece of chocolate and then looked at Pagey. Leaving the laxative chocolate bar on the table, Pagey then took a packet of cigarettes from his pocket and put one to his mouth, all the while staring at the chimp. Mitch returned the stare.

It was like watching Sam Spade light up a cigarette while engrossed in thought about an important case. The image was ruined when Page used his lighter which thrust a spear of flame past his nose singeing his own eyebrows.

"Bastard thing," said Page. Leaving the cigarette in the corner of his mouth, Pagey stood up and, taking the chocolate, walked with ponderous steps towards Mitch who bared his teeth. Page looked at the chimp and he too bared his teeth. Mitch suddenly looked in genuine fear and having established something of a presence, Page held out a piece of the chocolate. The chimp snatched it from his grasp and rammed it into his mouth, chewing vigorously. He then gulped and the chocolate was gone.

I smiled when Pagey broke another piece off the bar and handed it to the greedy chimp. Mitch thrust it into his mouth and in a gulp it too had gone. Pagey looked around rather surreptitiously before breaking off a double piece this time. I was about to intervene but it was too late because Mitch had already taken it.

Six pieces of chocolate later, it was all gone and Pagey turned to me with a broad grin of victory across his face.

"That'll teach the bastard to spit at me. Bloody ape!" he said.

Rik then returned from the bar and Mitch bounded onto his shoulder. The pair of them then went to the dressing rooms to change into their stage suits and prepare for their moment in the spotlight.

"That bloody monkey'll fart for England when that stuff gets hold. It works on the old folks within fifteen minutes, so Christ knows what it will do to that bloody monkey," Page announced triumphantly.

Just then, I heard the sound of three bells indicating that the show would start in three minutes. We finished our drinks and went into the main auditorium. Our seats were about five rows from the front and we were in a prime position for what was to follow.

The master of ceremonies for the evening was an old stager with false teeth which clicked when he spoke. He introduced Rik Romola with considerable relish and on came Rik to the music of a souped up version of 'Tea For Two' cha-cha-cha style.

As he danced his way across the stage, he threw down packs of cards which appeared to be coming from each of his sleeves, but then much to the delight of some of the youngsters in the audience, as if from nowhere, he produced Mitch, the flatulent monkey.

It was quite apparent that the animal was already in some discomfort, and as he was on Rik's shoulder, the radio microphone was picking up the odd fart or two.

There was some giggling and whispering among the younger members of the audience until Pagey stood up and shouted, "I do believe that monkey is farting in time with the music."

This was the signal for the whole audience to start laughing. Rik had never had this kind of attention before and Mitch became more agitated. He started to pull cards out of Rik's breast pocket for which he received rapturous applause. Mitch could not help himself and as he leaned over to get a monkey nut as a reward for his trick, it happened. The entire audience discovered the power of laxative chocolate when the whole of the left side front of Rik's white suit became awash with liquified chimpanzee excrement. The shocked silence only lasted a second until the laughter rolled round the theatre once more. In a bemused state, Rik continued his act and Mitch switched shoulders to snatch a bunch of flowers that had magically appeared and began to throw them at the audience. He was then beset with a further bout of laxative induced embarrassment and the right-hand side of poor old Rik's white suit was covered in a huge stain to match the left. With classical timing, two white doves then appeared and settled on Rik's outstretched hands just as Mitch released the biggest fart of the evening which unfortunately coincided with another very moist bowel movement. With a synchronised flapping of their wings two brown polka-dotted doves flew to sanctuary offstage as Rik took his bows from the most ecstatic and appreciative audience of his career.

"My God!" How do I follow that?" a very nervous Max Crapper mumbled to himself as he psyched himself up to follow Rik. "At least the magician has warmed them up for me," he thought.

He could hear the guffaws of the audience still echoing around the hall as the master of ceremonies tried to make himself heard above the packed house in front of him. He waited for them to calm down and then took a deep breath before announcing "And now, ladies and gentlemen, to send you home with a smile on your face, our very own cheeky chappy, Max Crapper!!"

He had just managed to get the words out when he realised that he had taken a deep breath in through his nostrils and had inhaled the foul smell that was now hanging over the whole of the stage area. He just had time to turn away from the microphone, when he vomited with such force that his false teeth shot across the stage in the direction of the side curtain from where Max would make his appearance.

In the wings, Max had heard a great burst of laughter when his name had been announced and so, believing the moment was right he took a few steps back to begin his customary run on to the stage. He had just cleared the side curtains when he glanced down and saw a pair of teeth smiling up at him. He tried to avoid stepping on them but overstretched and slipped on something wet and slimy on the floor. He then skidded across the stage and was surprised to see the master of ceremonies standing right in front of him. It was too late to do anything and as he whipped the poor man's feet from under him, the man was sick again. Max then fell heavily backwards hitting his head on the stage. The noise reverberated in his head but as he drifted into unconsciousness this was replaced by the sound of the audience laughing and clapping and as the blackness surrounded him he was sure that he heard them stamping their feet and chanting, "We want the Max Crapper! We want the Max Crapper......!

The stage manager realised that something had gone wrong and decided to bring down the curtain and put the house lights on. He took one look at Max and phoned for an ambulance.

The audience had never seen anything like it before and as we all made our way out of the Civic Theatre, the talk was of nothing but Rik Romola and Mitch. Pagey smiled and with a wicked glint in his eye said, "When I saw the programme I thought Max Crapper was another act, not just a description of Rik's assistant."

Tenbelly said that a spectacle like that really gives you an appetite and so, although the rest of us could not agree we looked for a taxi to take us to Bob Ego's place. As we were waiting, the ambulance arrived and Max was carried out on a stretcher. He was still unconscious but had a serene smile on his face.

"Isn't that strange?" said Pagey. "The story I was going to tell you about Max and laxative chocolate at school also ended with him being taken away in an ambulance."

I could see that Sean Page felt not one twinge of guilt about his part in the affair. In any case, we had to move on to the serious part of the evening: serious eating and serious drinking.

The following day, back at work and feeling a little the worse for the night before, Wilf and I reviewed our situation.

There was plenty of work coming in, the bank was happy and the VAT man was taking his ill-gotten gains with the relish that only payment on time can bring. We were on the up and we believed that no-one could stand in our way.

If there was a spectre at the feast it was maybe the number of feasts themselves that was the problem. The 'grog' bottles were in constant supply but we knew we could handle it and the only problem was when we ran out! Our boozing did not affect our work and the success we were enjoying was more of an intoxicant than the contents of any bottle. I went to work with a spring in my step and a whistle on my lips.

The weekends were spent at home, working in the garden on Saturday followed by a night out, leaving Sunday as a day to recover from the week's excesses.

I was thirty four years old, reasonably fit but carrying a little too much weight, although my regular training sessions on the football pitch with Bader Lidster and the gang helped to keep it under control.   And so I viewed 1983 in eager anticipation, knowing that the times were a-changing, and such changes were not always for the best.

We had settled into our new offices and our practice was under control even though we had some new members of staff who had to learn the ropes.

There was always one person who could be relied on to let everyone know what should be done.   That person was our cleaner, Mrs Mott.

We first employed Mrs Mott in November 1981.   Until then our secretary, Ann, carried out such tasks, but as we got busier we decided to employ a professional.   We couldn't get one, so Mrs Mott arrived.

Early one cold spring morning while I was opening the post, she reminded me of her considerable presence.

"Our Martin loves that job," said Mrs. Mott, speaking with a cigarette dangling precariously from her mouth.

"Ee's never late........ee's even always early.......ee'll work overtime when ee can get it...........aye, ee's a good lad our Martin."

I was trying to read my letters but our beloved Mrs Mott was determined to talk...and when she was in the mood there was no stopping her.

"Are you busy then Mr Smith?" she asked, not really caring about the reply.

"Yes I am," I replied, in the certain knowledge that my protestations were of no value.

"I have a very busy day today and I really ought to get stuck in straight away",

"Aye," countered Mrs. Mott, "I can always tell when you are busy."

"How?" I asked.

"Ow what?" repeated Mrs. Mott.

"How can you tell when I am busy?"

"You squint", she said "With your eyes."

I had no answer for her and so I returned to my letters.   But before I could read one paragraph.......

"It's like vomit," she said demonstratively.

"What is?" I queried, somewhat confused at the protestation.

"Work........"

"Work?" I replied.

"Aye.   When it's got to be done, it's got to be done."

"Of course," I said, trying to humour her.

"Aye, that's our Martin," said Mrs. Mott.

"What, vomit?" I asked.

"No. Work," said Mrs. Mott.   "Work, work, work, I'nt it."

A short silence caused me to look up to find Mrs Mott sucking upon her cigarette.   She unintentionally blew the smoke in my direction causing me to cough.

"Aye. Ee loves that job our Martin.   Ee loves it."

I knew she wanted me to ask and I knew she probably wouldn't go until I did so.

"All right," I said, "What does he do?"

Mrs. Mott inhaled again, coughed and after a pause, said

"Ee kills pigs!"

"Kills pigs?" I replied.

"Aye.   Kills pigs, dead, finished, the lot."

"What for?" I queried for want of something better to say.

"For the abattoir," she stated, Kills 'em dead."   As if to underline the point, Mrs. Mott drew her thumb across her throat, like a murderer's threat.

There was another pause.   She inhaled yet again and completed a series of coughs.

"Aye, work, work, work, pig, pig, pig......dead, dead, dead." She spluttered and coughed and coughed.

"Enjoys his job does he?" I continued in the hope she might go away.

"Oh aye," she said "Loves it." I almost joined Mrs. Mott for a chorus of...........

"Pig, pig, pig, dead, dead, dead."

She had an annoying habit of repeating everything she said, yet, there was something endearing about her.` She had not really relished life, except for the birth of her five children, who were her pride and joy.   Unfortunately her marriage had floundered after twenty-five years, leaving her and her husband to go their separate ways.   Despite being apart for thirteen years she missed him and I suspect he missed her too. Mr Mott worked in the mines on permanent nights and had found the substitution of his wife for coal as company rather difficult to bear, which caused him to retreat with ever greater frequency to the sanctuary of his local haven, the pub.

As I looked at Mrs Mott for a moment, I saw a once pretty face, worn by the stresses of life.   She should have retired at sixty but necessity found her working into her sixty-third year. She had an honest face, still attractive for a woman of her age, which was illuminated by the most striking emerald green eyes I had ever seen.   She had kept her figure, a feat made the more remarkable by five child births and her daily intake of dripping breadcakes.   She put this down to being "regular", something upon which I never sought elaboration.   She was one of the most hard working and loyal women I had ever met, extremely proud and with considerable dignity.   The more I thought about it, the more I realised we had to put up with her.

My thoughts were disturbed by a further utterance.

"Now our Malcolm...!" She paused for a second, "We call him Talcolm. He's another good worker he is." I took a deep breath and sighed in defeat for I knew she was going to continue.

"Why do you call him Talcolm?" I asked slowly, with the certain knowledge that she would tell me anyway

"Because of where he works."

"Where's that?"

"Sewerage works!" She continued triumphantly, "Ee shovels............"

Before she could finish, I invited her to make some tea. She coughed and left.

Most of our morning interludes followed the same pattern. She would clean my room while handing out her homespun philosophy with complete disregard for my workload or anything else which required my consideration.

My tea arrived minus the sugar. I always have sugar in my tea, except when Mrs Mott made it.

"I've not put sugar in Mr. Smith, no wonder you're carrying all that weight. You want to use sweeteners like me, they are the best thing are sweeteners. All my lads use sweeteners."

I had mouthed the words in unison, having heard them before so many times.

"What about the one at the sewerage works?" I asked, "Does he use them?"

"Yes," said Mrs. Mott.

"Well then, I'll stick to sugar," I said and with that she left the office.

When she returned with the sugar, I thanked her only to be told,

"I can't stand here talking to you all day I've got work to do." She huffed and puffed out of the room as if to make the point that it was me who was stopping her from getting on with her work.

I then heard the sound of someone tripping over the Hoover on the landing, followed by much cursing and swearing. Wilf had arrived.

I opened his door to find the aftermath of the boozing session of the previous night. There were empty beer cans and the remains of two bottles of Canadian Club whisky spread over the threadbare Persian carpet. Streamers and one of those things you blow which unravels itself until it squeaks hung from the lights.

Wilf looked at me and sat back in his chair.

"I must have eaten something dodgy last night," he said in an attempt to hide a massive hangover.

"You don't think you have eaten one of the cans as well as having emptied them all do you?" I asked smirking.

"Piss off," he replied, "Can't you see I'm not well." His face was grey and his eyes were puffed up as if he had risen from sleep rather abruptly and far too early.

I then noticed a picture above his fireplace. It was not framed but merely fastened to the wall with a drawing pin. The subject bore a remarkable likeness to the Second World War Italian dictator Benito Mussolini and in the bottom right hand corner there appeared to be an autograph with the dedication....

"To Wilf, with thanks for your help in Abyssinia. Love Benito."

The signature was not dated, but the handwriting looked remarkably like that of Sean Page.

"How long have you been in the Fascist Party?" I asked.

"What?" said Wilf with no enthusiasm whatsoever.

"The picture," I said, nodding towards Benito's figure.

Wilf looked at the wall, observed the picture and asked,

"What is it?"

I handed him his glasses, without which he was blind, and Wilf studied the picture thoughtfully before announcing,

"It's Mussolini."

Before I could respond, Mrs Mott joined us, looking for a duster.

"Excuse me gents, "I've lost me duster. Is it in 'ere?"

She noticed us looking at the picture and joined in as we studied it together.

"Hey," she said, "That's Pavorotti i'nt it?"

I looked at Wilford and he at me, and then we both looked at Mrs Mott.

"It's Benito Mussolini," I said. "The former fascist dictator of Italy who was strung up outside a petrol station in Milan having been shot by Italian patriots on April 28th 1945."

Mrs Mott paused for a moment and announced,

"Aye, Pavorotti that's him, he's a singer. He looks young there though, looks as though 'ees 'ad all 'is 'air shaved off. Aye that's him Pavarotti - that's when 'ee 'ad been in that show, what's it called er......aye 'King and I'. That's it, King and I."

With that, she picked up her cloth and walked out.

"She's got to go," said Wilf, "That woman drives me barmy, I'm sure she's been at our whisky cabinet."

Just then the door opened again,

"Aye, that's 'im, Pavarotti!"

I took the picture from the wall just in case we had any Italian patriots who might choose to visit us. I left Wilf with a large mug of tea and three Anadins, before setting off to face the hostilities in the Rotherham Magistrates' Court.

As I walked up the stone stairs to the Court, I noticed a group of Asian gentlemen standing at the top of the stairs huddled together in conversation. As I walked past, the conversation stopped and a voice shouted out in a broad Yorkshire accent, "Ay up, tha Steve Smith ain't tha?"

I turned to the youngest of the group, who would be a man about 20 years old and was wearing a large white frock type garment and a strange hat. I noted that his accent did not match his dress. He beamed at me and told me that his brother was locked up in the cells,

"It's our Tariq tha knows, e's locked up tha sees and we want thee to represent 'im, if tha sees what I mean like."

I would have loved to have replied in Punjabi, but unfortunately I was unable to do so. I was then introduced to his father, his uncle, his brother, his cousin, his stepbrother, the local Holy man and an interpreter. The supporter's club followed me into the court room and I found them places from where they would be able to see the proceedings.

My morning visits to the cells were always delightful experiences. The last time any of the walls saw a lick of paint would have been at the time of the Coronation. I am thinking of course of the coronation of Edward VII.

The newly appointed jailer was PC Kemp, an old stager with over thirty years experience. He was living proof that PC's never die, they just end up at Rotherham Court House cells. PC Kemp was an honest man with a great deal of integrity.

"Alreight love," he said, "Who does tha want to see?"

I gave him the list of three prisoners and he promptly brought out someone who I had never seen before and was not on the list.

"I don't act for this man Derek," I said, "I think he's represented by someone else."

"Alreight then love, who do you want then?"

"How about one of those on the list I gave you," I said with a touch of sarcasm.

"OK love," answered PC Kemp, failing to notice my jibe, and promptly brought Tariq out to see me.

Tariq was about nineteen years old, short of stature with jet black hair and eyes which looked suspiciously around the room. Quite who he was looking for I don't know, but I got the distinct impression he thought that someone else would be there.

He handed me his charge sheet and I read that the police were alleging that he had taken three vehicles without consent. Unfortunately the last vehicle had been chased by the police and involved in a crash. I noted a wound to his forehead which had clearly been stitched and there was some blood staining on his colourful shirt.

He explained to me how he had gone out with two other youths and they had decided to steal a car. Tariq did not want to be involved, but unfortunately the peer pressure was too great to resist and he reluctantly agreed to join in. He explained that he had simply got into the car after the other two lads had taken it and was driven off.

Tariq had got to know the other youths, who were white and lived nearby, and had only joined in because he was afraid that if he didn't he would be ostracised. His father was furious as they were a good hard working family with no previous convictions whatsoever and it was difficult for them to accept the shame their son had brought upon their house.

His father represented the old ways, which meant that the children were expected to keep out of trouble and be extremely respectful to their elders. But times were changing and the second generation of Asians were growing up and finding it difficult to live by the old ways developed over many centuries in a country they had never seen. However, the family support within the Asian community is very strong, and this was made clear by the large deputation who had attended at court that day.

Unfortunately, Tariq had no option but to plead guilty, which meant that he would acquire a criminal record in the process: something which considerably upset the family. It was my job to try to keep the penalty down to a minimum on a guilty plea. I suspected that the real punishment would be inflicted on Tariq when he left court, a point which I put to the bench before they came to their own conclusions.

My next client was a rather unsavoury looking gentleman from the biking fraternity. He wore a leather jacket and filthy denim jeans which looked as thought they could have walked in on their own had he not been wearing them. He had long straggly hair which looked like it had last seen a shower when he had walked through one. His beard was long and tangled and seemed to stretch up his face beyond his cheeks to the base of his eye sockets. His eyebrows were in a similar state and he spoke with a growl as if perpetually trying to clear his throat. There was a very heavy smell of Petulia oil about him, a perfumed substance used by many to cover up the smell of cannabis.

He sat down and produced two charge sheets from his jacket pocket which looked as though they had been rolled in oil and gravy. I delicately opened them at a distance as if they concealed some infectious disease, to find that he had been charged with G.B.H. (grievous bodily harm).

"If you think I'm pleading guilty to these you can kiss my arse," he said defiantly as I looked up having read the charge sheets.

"I would prefer not to thank you, I'm trying to give it up. Instead, tell me what happened…"

I moved further up the bench away from my evil smelling client in the hope that it might remove my desire to vomit.

"I was minding me own business when this stupid landlord came up and suggested that I was smoking cannabis. I said 'knackers' and 'e took offence. 'e told me to leave and I refused because I 'ad't finished my pint and I wasn't putting up with 'is kind of manner. 'e reached down to take 'old of me arm, and nobody touches me, so I cracked 'im."

"Well that makes you guilty of assault doesn't it?" I asked.

"Fuck off," said the biker indignantly, "I were defending mesen. 'e touched me, so I touched 'im."

"Yes, he touched you with the tip of his finger on your arm and you hit him in the teeth with your fist. According to this charge sheet, you have knocked three of his teeth out."

"Fuck off," said the biker, equally as indignant as before.

"What's the assault on the police officer about?"

"Well, I left the pub see, and then, as I were walking down the road to me bike, a squad car came screaming up, this young copper came up and took 'old of me arm, and nobody does that, so I....."

"Cracked him?" I interposed.

"Correct," said the biker.

"Self defence, I suppose."

"Correct," said the biker. "I want out man, I want my freedom, I want my rights, I want something to eat...and I want me cigs."

"Do you want anything else?" I asked. "A hacksaw, a file or a shower perhaps?"

"Look" snarled the biker, "I don't take kindly to cells, I don't take kindly to coppers and I don't take kindly to people who touch me. I just don't like being touched.

"I wouldn't have thought that would have been much of a problem for you," I said risking a crack myself. He missed the point of my comment so I continued.

"The first thing I will sort out is the question of bail, and then we will talk about whether you are guilty or not."

"OK man, stay cool," said the biker, who clearly was unable to take his own advice.

My third prisoner was a lady who had not paid her fine for failure to possess a television licence. She was extremely tearful and explained that her husband had given her the money for the television licence but she had spent it on food. She was clearly in fear of him, and it seemed he knew nothing about the court appearance. She was certainly more terrified of him than the court so I agreed to get her case called on first so she could get home and possibly avoid her husband's wrath.

As I was about to leave the cells, PC Kemp called me back.

"Here Steve love there's another one in the cells for you, just brought him in. Drunk and Disorderly, Criminal Damage, Urinating in a Public Place and, oh yes, there's theft"

"What are the details Derek?" I asked.

"He got drunk, smashed a car up, nicked something out of the car and pissed in the street. There are two other lads with him, but it's just the one for you."

"What's this man's name?" I asked.

"Not sure, but I'll bring him in."

I went back into the interview room opposite the cells and got my papers out in readiness. The door opened and a young lad about 17 years old walked in. He had curly blond hair and a bright, clean complexion, apart from a massive lump over his left eye which was surrounded by heavy fresh bruising. It was a most substantial shiner. The other eye was clear and of the most unusual emerald green colour. He came in wearing a blood-stained white shirt and jeans. His head was bowed and he looked extremely sorry for himself.

"Sit down young man," I said, "And give me your sheets."

45

I looked at the charge sheets and read the name,

"Michael Morris ………," my voice tailed off as I read the surname,

"Mott."

I remained quiet for a second or two and then the realisation of who he was hit me.

I had to decide whether to express recognition or not as I didn't wish to embarrass him. Fortunately, the decision was taken from me.

"You're Steve Smith aren't you?" said the young man

"Yes, I am, and you are Michael Mott," I replied.

"Yes, I am." He replied.

I was giving nothing else away and leaving it to him to decide whether to say anything. He had not realised that his secret was safe with me, as I suppose he had no understanding of legal etiquette and the duty of privacy that his case imposed upon me. He could clearly stand it no longer and eventually announced.

"My mum works for you."

"Does she really?" I said in reply.

"Yes, Mrs. Mott, your cleaner."

"Oh" I said feigning surprise "I hadn't realised that."

"Aye, she'll kill me if she knows where I am, but I didn't know anybody else when the jailer asked if I knew a solicitor. Your name was the first that came into my head."

I immediately put his mind at rest.

"Don't worry Michael, I won't say anything, and certainly not to your mum."

"Thank God," he said, "She'd kill me," leaving me in no doubts as to his anxiety and concern.

I asked him to recount his story and while he did so I checked the antecedent history which the jailer had given to me. It described him as a 17 year old youth, employed with no previous convictions whatsoever.

He explained that he had been out with some of his friends and had had some drink at a party. He told me how there had been a competition as to who could drink the party cocktail in one go. It was clear that a lethal concoction had been prepared and Michael had tried it.....repeatedly.

"I can't really remember everything that happened," said Michael, "But my mates damaged a car, took something out of it and threw it at me. Someone shouted "run" and the next thing I remember was trying to run down the street. After a few yards I had to stop because I was busting for a 'wee'. I stood in a doorway and had just started when a bobby grabbed me. I urinated all down my trousers so I complained to him and I think that I pushed him in the chest, but I am not sure. The next thing that I knew I was in the police station."

"How did you get the black eye?" I asked.

With his head bowed he explained how the officer had struck him a blow in the face.

"Why did he do that?" I asked.

"I suppose I asked for it," said Master Mott. "After all, I pushed him so I don't suppose that I left him with any alternative. Look Mr Smith, if my mother gets to know about this, my feet won't touch the floor."

"Yes I suppose that's true Michael," I said, trying to be sympathetic, "But you have really brought this on yourself, although I'm worried about your black eye and the explanation as to how it happened."

"I'm not bothered about that Mr Smith, I asked for it and I got it All I want to do is get out of here and get sorted out."

He looked at me through his good eye before announcing,

"You'll never see me back in court again Mr Smith, I've learnt my lesson. I'm not bothered what they do to me, so long as they don't tell me mother."

He had a rather refreshing attitude towards his predicament. More often than not, lads with previous convictions are only worried about themselves and care little for the thoughts or well being of others. This lad was out of his depth. He had behaved out of character with a group who had led him astray and, what's more, he knew it.

I decided that I would try to deal with him, or as solicitors say, 'Weigh him off'. With a fair wind and a good bench I thought I might be able to do just that.

Unfortunately, there was to be no fair wind, nor good bench. I had 'dropped for' the Honourable Lord Chief Justice, my favourite magistrate. He didn't like me, I didn't like him, and we both knew how the other felt. There seemed little point in trying to weigh him off because the Lord Chief would want a probation officer to see Michael and prepare a report as to his background and consider a recommendation as to how the court should deal with the case. This would mean an adjournment and a visit by a probation officer to Michael's home. It would be a catastrophic consequence to a stupid, rather than criminal act and it would also embarrass Mrs Mott, so much so that I actually believed she would be unable to continue working for us as her pride would have been damaged beyond recovery.

For the first time, I felt incredibly sorry for her. She was a hard working woman who had given everything for her children. Her marriage had failed, but she still had her children of whom she was so very proud. I felt that without her pride in her children there would have been very little left for her.

I decided to deal with the biker first and then call Michael's case on afterwards. The object of the exercise was to allow the magistrate to vent his spleen on the 'bad guy' and then call on Michael's case when perhaps the bench had got the punishment factor out of their system.

The biker walked into Court and demonstrated a marked reluctance to show any respect at all. Although he did not realise it at the time, his behaviour had already sealed his fate. Quite rightly, the magistrate was entitled to respect for the nature of his office, but he didn't get any from my recalcitrant client.

I used every point that I could to secure bail and when my address had finished the bench retired. My client waived me over from the dock and after what I thought was a rather splendid bail application, I walked to him expecting some measure of thanks and appreciation.

I was greeted, however, in a very different vein,

"Tha didn't tell 'em me girlfriend's pregnant."

I couldn't help making a point;

"So what?"

My client was surprised at my reaction and it caught him on the back foot,

"So what?" he said "So what?, it's obvious in't it, she needs me."

"Yes," I thought to myself, "Just like I need impetigo."

"I don't think the fact that you have dropped some bird in the club is going to make any difference to whether this bench grants you bail or not. I think they will say if you thought anything about the girl you wouldn't have got into this trouble in the first place," I said.

"But I've got to be in to look after her," protested the biker.

"Anyway, whose side are you on?" he whined.

"Yours, that's why I'm not coming out with complete bollocks to the court."

I didn't like to use such language, but I thought he might be able to grasp my feelings if I put it to him in a fashion which he was more likely to understand.

"If I don't get bail, I'm kicking off," he announced, and with that the court sergeant who was standing nearby and had overheard the conversation radioed downstairs for reinforcements.

The new courthouses have a direct link from the cells to the dock and there is some measure of protection so that the prospects of escape are limited, but in 1983 a prisoner had to be brought from the cells, walked across the courtroom and into a dock, though it was not unknown for athletic defendants to wriggle out of handcuffs, vault the dock and run out of the building.

Within a very short time, the dock occupied not only my client and his guard, but three other very large police officers with a collective weight of almost 80 stones. The biker was grossly outnumbered.

Within a short time the magistrate returned to the court and announced that he was remanding my client in custody for fear that he would commit further offences. My client rose to his feet and gave forth a most vitriolic complaint which included the phrase,

"You fucking thick bastard, tha ought to be shot wi shit."

His latter point found some favour with me, but as I was considering its merits the fun really started. The biker refused to leave the dock, whereupon the tag team of 4 burly officers set about their work in enthusiastic fashion and he was manhandled towards the door, behind which was the spiral staircase leading to the cell area. Once the door was

50

closed, the clattering sounds of a man falling down stairs were heard, followed by a voice tailing off into the distance:

"Oh my goodness me, I hope you are not hurt......."

The court sergeant returned adjusting his tie and told me that my client wanted to see me as soon as he had been brought back from the hospital.

Young Mott was the next to arrive in court and he presented an entirely different picture.

With his head bowed, he entered a guilty plea to his charges and the prosecutor, an old friend of mine called John Brind, opened his case. John was a very good prosecutor but also an excellent musician, and we would spend much of our time talking about music when we should have been discussing cases. We found that we could discuss work very quickly and reach an agreement, leaving us free to concentrate on more important things.

I decided I would suggest to the magistrate that he would need a report from a probation officer before Michael's case could be dealt with. I anticipated that he would do entirely the opposite to what I had recommended and, sure enough, he ran true to character.

"No, I don't think so Mr Smith. This is clearly a case that we can deal with today," he said smiling smugly.

I willingly yielded to the Lord Chief's request and proceeded to mitigate the case, pointing out what a good lad and hard worker he was and every other point I could think of before listening to the magistrate sentence him.

After the case I went to the cells to see Michael before he left. He had been fined £100.00, but his only worry was where the fine notice would be sent. He explained that his mother always opened his mail and if she saw the notice she would realise what had happened. I told him that I would see the magistrates' clerk and collect the fine notice myself on the understanding that Michael came to my office at the end of the week, picked it up and made his payments directly to the court.

I returned to the court and looked with horror as I saw a reporter from the local newspaper, The Rotherham Advertiser, copying the list of charges from the court list.

Before I could say anything, the reporter had gone, armed with enough information to castigate the unfortunates who had appeared there that day.

I considered speaking to the reporter and asking him not to print the story, but I thought that might draw his attention to it and thus prompt a report. I decided to keep matters to myself and hope for the best.

The Rotherham Advertiser is published on Fridays and is circulated to many thousands of homes. On the Friday morning, when I went into the office, I noticed that the paper had arrived and was on the reception counter.

Mrs Mott was busy with her hoover only a few feet away. Before she noticed anything I picked it up and took it into my office. This was one paper she was not going to see that morning.

I quickly scanned each page to see if I could find any reference to the case and my heart sank when I turned to page seven and saw the sub headline "DRUNKEN YOB STEALS FROM CAR." I realised that it would be only a matter of time before she got to know unless I did something about it. No one would have the courage to tell her, so I thought the secret safe. I couldn't just hide the paper as Mrs Mott was in the habit of taking it home after work on Mondays, so I tore out page seven, screwed it up and was about to throw it in the bin when a photograph of a monkey caught my eye. It was Mitch and the headline read, 'MITCH SAVED FROM DEATH ROW'. I straightened out the paper and read that

Max Crapper, the well-known local comedian had been involved in an accident at the Civic Theatre. He had been unconscious for two days after a nasty fall which police believed had happened after he had been savagely attacked by a performing chimpanzee. Max had received a serious head wound but could not remember much of what had happened before the fall. The police had discovered that the chimp was known to be aggressive and had been told that on the night in question, it had been quite ill. They believed that Max's injury had been caused by a bite and indeed a piece of tooth had been found embedded in the back of his skull. With all this evidence against the chimp, the police issued a summons with which Rik had to comply within a given period.

Rik was mortified. His relationship with his assistant was far from harmonious but Mitch was all he had and anyway he had just spent a fortune in vet's bills trying to clear up a 'tummy bug' the chimp must have picked up somewhere.

However, when Rik took Mitch back to the same vet for the lethal injection, the vet told him that Mitch had perfect teeth and certainly no recently broken ones. Rik asked the vet to ring the police who were very reluctant to believe that Max could have been bitten so severely by anything else but they eventually agreed to ask a forensic expert to examine the piece of tooth taken from Max's skull. The result, when it came, was a surprise to everyone. Max's head had been viciously gnawed by a pair of false teeth.

Mitch was saved and Rik was a happy man but in view of what had happened and because he couldn't afford a new stage suit, Rik had decided to retire Mitch and let him live out his days at a monkey sanctuary in the south of England. This had been suggested by the R.S.P.C.A. who had visited Rik following an anonymous phonecall which had implied that Mitch had been ill-treated during a show at the Civic Theatre.

Having read the full account of how forensic science saved Mitch the monkey from an irrevocable miscarriage of justice, I once again screwed up the paper and threw it in the bin. I put the paper on top of the fish tank and got on with my work. Alongside Mitch's account, the story of a drunken young man's stupidity would be dead, dead, dead by Monday.

Chapter Four

SHE MAY BE UGLY, BUT JANE CAN'T HALF FEIGHT

When Wilf and I set up in business together the thought of ever having too many clients never entered our heads. In the early days we would have been pleased with one each but in the spring of 1983 I was beginning to realise that a successful practice can be a nightmare at times. Some days it seemed that certain clients expected me to be available to them alone twenty four hours a day. Being in two places at once had already been written into my job description and sleep was becoming a luxury I snatched between late night visits to various police stations and long working days rushing between the office and the magistrates court.

I was as keen as ever but I found my patience with some of my clients was wearing a bit thin. The more I did for them, the more they seemed to demand. However, the thing that made it all worthwhile was the knowledge that once in a while, among the mass of routine cases there would be one that would be special. There are many factors which make a case special for me and it isn't always related to the seriousness of the case. It could be the personality of the client, the nature of the crime or an unusual aspect of a particular point of law which will make a case special. There is, however one category of crime which is always special. For the aficionado there is no case quite like murder.

One bright late March morning I overslept having spent most of the night in Maltby police station helping an ungrateful client. Arriving at the office at 9.15am I knew that it was going to be a bad day which was destined to get worse as fatigue set in.

I had promised to dictate a brief to counsel and deliver it to the barrister's chambers by 10am. I could not find the file and my dictaphone appeared to have buggered off somewhere. "Who's got my bloody dictaphone?" I shouted down the corridor.

There was no answer.

"Is everybody dead?" I demanded. Obviously they were because no one answered, at least not until Mrs Mott peered around my door.

"Morning Mr Smith. You're late this morning..........one too many last night eh?........You want to watch that..............Got my husband that, you know. Eventually at least, but got him it did poor old bugger......He's been gone fifteen years now......."

I interrupted Mrs Mott's persistent monologue.

"I didn't know your husband was dead?" I said, trying to be considerate.

"He isn't dear. Oh no, he's gone alright, but not up there," she said, laughing and looking at the ceiling. "He's gone to his sister's.......yes," she said thoughtfully.

"It's been fifteen years now...........He still drinks and smokes like a trooper.........I don't know how she stands it."

"Who?" I asked, pretending to be interested.

"His sister..........Mindst you, she's as bad as him.............It's terrible."

I then found the file I had been looking for, only to return to my desk to find the ubiquitous Mrs Mott oblivious to my desire to do some work.

"It makes your clothes stink," she said demonstratively.

"What does?" I asked.

"Cig smoke!"

"Oh I see, in smokey rooms you mean?"

"Filthy habit that, without doubt that is a filthy habit," she said, just as Jack Bennett entered my office.

"What is?" asked Jack, coming in at a confusing part of the conversation.

"He knows," she said, nodding at me, and with that off she went, hoovering the corridor for all she was worth.

"What have you been up to now?" asked Jack. "Which of your filthy habits have you subjected her to?" he said, laughing.

"Setting fire to cleaners?" I replied.

Jack was still confused.

"May I ask what you're doing here?" said Jack.

"What do you mean?" I asked earnestly.

"Well I thought you were in Sheffield Crown Court this morning doing a bail application?" I thought for a moment and then felt beads of sweat appear around my forehead and temples as the realisation struck that I had forgotten to put the application in my diary. It looked like I was in for a grade three bollocking.

I went to the filing cabinet to get the file and, of course, because it was urgent and I was late and desperate, I couldn't find it.

"F…..who has got the Morton file?" I shouted.

No-one answered and I lost my temper. Eventually it turned up, but not before I had kicked the filing cabinet and tripped over the telephone wire.

I ran out of the office to my car, which had been blocked in by a bread van. Eventually I escaped and set off through town like the proverbial bat out of hell. I wonder why it is that when you are in a rush you get stuck behind twelve learner drivers, five JCBs and two broken down milk floats. Eventually I got to the car park near the court. It was full. I had dispensed my entire vocabulary of swear words by the time I found a parking place and I was still a quarter of a mile from the court. There was nothing else to do but to start running and with about a minute to spare I reached the court. I ran up the stairs to court number three where an usher was waiting for me.

"Mr Smith," I announced with a wheeze, "Bail application, Morton, before Judge Walker, and have you got an iron lung?"

"Don't worry Mr Smith, the judge won't be here for another thirty minutes. He's been delayed in traffic!" said the usher firmly, as though I should have known.

I slumped back on the seat outside the courtroom and wiped perspiration from my brow with an ink stained handkerchief.

"I have risked prosecution and a coronary to get here on time, and he's late!" I explained with annoyance.

"Yes," said the usher, "You have. Oh and by the way, you've got ink on your forehead."

I cursed under my breath.

"And you." said the usher as she walked away.

Fifteen minutes later I was called into the judge's chambers to find him, with not a bead of sweat on him. On the other hand, I was saturated, with my hair gripping my scalp with unlimited affection.

The judge peered over his horn rimmed glasses and said,

"Are you alright, Mr, er Smith?"

"Perfectly your Honour," I replied, wiping even more perspiration from my brow.

"Looks like a virus to me," said the judge, surveying the dampened object before him.

"Yes your Honour," I replied. There appeared to be little point in arguing.

"Well I've looked at your bail application Mr Smith," said the judge.

"Thank you your Honour," I replied expectantly.   I had long since learned to speak when I was spoken to.

"He's a wicked man," said the judge, "And wicked men must go to prison.   I cannot see any possibility of a non-custodial sentence for this man, so he shall remain in custody."

The learned judge made his point forcefully, although I would have preferred to have had a bit of a say myself.

When I suggested that there may be good reasons for granting bail, the judge pointed out that he had read my written submissions and found no favour with them, and unless I could introduce anything over and above that which I had put in the written application, he was not going to reverse his decision.   In fairness, I was only able to repeat what I had written and had no option but to say so.

"Well then," said the judge, "I will repeat it again for your benefit.   He will be remanded in custody on the grounds that he will commit further offences if he should be granted bail. Next case."

I left the judge's chambers feeling that, while he had got the right decision, I wasn't too happy about the way that he went about giving it, but then I suppose that was his prerogative.

I ran down to the magistrates court and, using the old pals act, managed to jump the queue, apart from one solicitor who was not prepared to assist me in any way.   He wanted to do his case and then spend half an hour in the tea room.

A solicitor who had let me push in was sat directly behind me and when I eventually finished my case, I turned to him and said,

"Thanks a lot.   When you come to Rotherham I will do the same for you."

As I rushed out of the court I almost fell over the solicitor who had been less obliging and said exactly the same to him.

I left the Sheffield Magistrates' Court at 11.30, arriving back in Rotherham twenty minutes later. I ran into the court room to be greeted by the emphysemic usher.

"Brilliant timing Steve, there is just one case left and then it's you."

"Do you mean there is no bollocking?"

"Yes," said the usher, "No bollocking at all, except perhaps a grade one from your clients."

"Oh, I can deal with that," I said and promptly called out the names of the people I was to represent.

I recognised all but one name, which was a file Jack had prepared and had put in the diary for that morning. Looking for my client, I spotted an unusual looking person in a dark suit with an Elvis Presley haircut.

"I'm Jane," said Elvis in a rather deep and melodious voice.

We shook hands and she crushed my knuckles, making me wince with pain.

We went to the 'rat hole' interview room and I realised that this was an adjournment in order that we could obtain the evidence from the prosecution and consider how best to approach the case. It was an assault case which occurred in a night club only a matter of a few days before. I had not had time to consider the details because the file had only been brought up to court for me that morning and I had not had chance to read it. The charge sheet referred to an 'S. Clarke,' so I asked my client, "What's Miss Clarke's first name?" believing that it was an assault upon another lady.

"Simon Clarke," she replied, "And he's no lady."

"Oh, right," I said, acknowledging my mistake. "Well the case is going to be adjourned today so that we can see what the evidence is against you, but please tell me what happened?"

60

She explained that she had been in the night club and, because of her dress and hairstyle, this youth had made some rather insulting remarks which my client had taken to heart.

"I must admit I got rather upset with something he said."

"What was that?" I asked naively.

"He said, 'He's a big bugger and he's got his own tits as well'. I hate sexist remarks like that and I was not being humiliated by him or anybody, so I lamped him."

I later found out that she had lamped him extremely well, removing three of his front teeth and leaving his lip requiring four stitches.

"I only hit him once, but it was a good un," said my client, totally understating the position.

When I got into court, I handed in my client's criminal record, which contained a number of convictions for assault, wounding and threatening behaviour.

The prosecutor requested an adjournment because he was waiting for a further statement from a dentist who would confirm the extent of the treatment needed to replace the lost teeth. I agreed the adjournment, which would enable me to take further instructions and sort out the question of my client's previous convictions.

When we came out into the corridor, I advised Jane very briefly about bail and the requirement to return to court on the date that she had been given. Unfortunately, some idiot behind me passed a sexist remark. Jane's eyes narrowed and flashed in search of the culprit.

"Who said that?" she demanded in an angry tone.

No-one answered and I ushered Jane away.

There was no doubt that Jane's temper had a hair trigger. She was a time bomb waiting to go off and it was no surprise to me that she was well known to the courts. She was a woman of considerable physical strength and had a fearless nature, which was going to lead her into further trouble.

The same evening I met with Jarvis and Co. at Reilley's restaurant for our monthly soiree. Bob and Lynn, the owners, were extremely likeable people and, as well as providing excellent food and service they also had a forgiving and tolerant nature.

After warning my companions that I would not be able to join in the more serious drinking due to a very important football match the following day, by the end of the evening I realised that I had indeed seriously enjoyed myself, so much so that the following morning I felt dreadful.

I could not shake off the hangover, despite drinking many bottles of mineral water. At 5.30pm after a difficult day I set off to the match, changing in the car when I arrived at the ground.

We were playing the Probation Service team, who were intelligent, courteous and kindly people at work, but vicious fouling morons on the football field. In the first fifteen minutes, I had at least three clear chances to score, but I fluffed each one.

Bader Lidster came up to me just before a free kick and asked me what was wrong.

"I feel like death," I told him.

"Is it a virus?" asked Bader, sympathetically.

"Yes, I suppose you could say that Bader. At any rate the effects are fairly similar." A little later in the game, we were awarded a free kick for yet another foul.

"You take this one cocker, " said Bader.

I looked into the distance and saw the biggest goalkeeper in the world. My accuracy left a lot to be desired that day, so I thought that if I aimed directly for him, the ball might go near to one of the posts. I took six or seven paces, ran up to the ball and mis-kicked it. It spun off the side of my foot, arced round three players in the defensive wall and shot into the top left hand corner of the net like a guided missile. All the team congratulated me and even our opponents gave a round of applause.

"Tha's taking all t' free kicks from now on," said Bader. "I have niver seen a ball struck like that before."

I ran to the touchline and was violently sick. I returned to the game and scored two more goals before coming off with ten minutes to go. I was knackered.

After the match we went to the pub, where I ordered two bitter lemons and a sandwich. Bader came back with an egg, tomato and dripping sandwich. It was marvellous. There is something to be said about the "hair of the dog" and two pints of Guinness later, I felt on top form.

After the match I decided to go back to the office to collect some papers for a case I was dealing with the following day, as I wanted to prepare for it overnight. I had just picked up the papers and was about to leave when the telephone rang. You should never answer the telephone in an office after 5.30pm because it always leads to trouble. Unfortunately, I broke the rule on this occasion to be told that my client Jane had been involved in an altercation in a working mens' club. Another girl had been seriously injured when a broken glass had slashed her neck. She had lost a very substantial amount of blood, and was in a critical condition. I had no alternative but to go to the police station, see my client and obtain an update as to the girl's medical position before considering the best course of action.

I arrived at the charge office to see a stern faced custody sergeant Brown reaching for his telephone.

"Sergeant Brown, custody suite," he announced into the handset.

"Yes Sir, her solicitor has just arrived. No Sir, she had not been told yet, I rather thought I might let Mr Smith tell her……"

As Sergeant Brown listened to his instructions a shiver ran down my spine. "What had she not been told," I wondered. Sergeant Brown continued………………

"Very good Sir, I'll ask him to wait a moment while you join us - very good Sir."

He turned to me, but it was not a cheerful welcome.

"What's wrong Dave?" I asked cautiously.

"Better wait for Chief Inspector Varey," said the sergeant, "I'm under orders."

"What's going on?" I asked when Chief Inspector Varey arrived, grim faced. Before he could speak, I had realised what had happened.

"She's dead isn't she, the girl in Jane Webb's case, she's dead?"

The Chief Inspector gave sergeant Brown an accusatory glare.

"Not said a word Sir, I think Mr Smith worked it out."

"He's right," I said, jumping to the sergeant's defence. "When?" I asked.

"About an hour ago. Death was due to haemorrhage and shock. The main artery was severed and the blood loss was too great. The hospital did their best but it was too late. It was her birthday tomorrow. She would have been twenty-one years old. Happy birthday, eh?"

I sat in the chair usually occupied by defendants who were to have their photographs taken for CID records. A detective sergeant who I knew walked in, unaware of the news.

"Got you at last Mr Smith have they? What have you done then; drink driving, impersonating a solicitor or flashing..........?"

The sergeant then became aware of Chief Inspector Varey.

"I'm, sorry Sir. I didn't see you.........It was only a joke...........Well, I'll be off then. Bye for now..."

He looked at me, shrugged his shoulders and left as quickly as he came.

I looked at the Chief Inspector and broke the silence.

"I take it she doesn't know?" I queried, nodding towards the female cells.

"No, she doesn't," said Chief Inspector Varey. "We thought you might want to tell her, and then I'm afraid we have got to do an interview. Of course, if you prefer me to............"

His words tailed off in the expectation I would offer.

"OK, I'll see her. Which cell is she in?"

I was directed to the female cell where I found Jane sitting cross legged, a forlorn and lonely figure.

Her eyes lit up somewhat when she saw me enter.

Unfortunately, I could not return her smile, and she realised that I was not the bearer of good news. It was almost as if telepathy had taken over as we looked at each other. The silence seemed interminable, until Jane spoke.

"You've got something to tell me haven't you?"

I looked away without speaking, but she knew and burst into tears.

I didn't say anything but simply sat beside her. Her hard exterior crumbled before my eyes as her body shook with her sobs. She was completely distraught and I knew there was nothing I could say to help her.

After some time she quietened and I handed her a packet of cigarettes which she smoked furiously. As she finished one she lit another, and then another, until the cell was full of thick smoke.

I chose a moment to ask Jane to tell me what had happened. The tough veneer had gone but so had her ability to speak. I asked her if I could get her a drink and she nodded so I rang the cell bell and managed to open the door to allow some fresh air to enter the seven foot by seven foot room. The jailer brought a glass of weak orange cordial, which Jane drank without taking a breath. It was apparent that she was suffering from dehydration brought on by the considerable amount of alcohol she had drunk the night before.

I persuaded the custody sergeant to allow us to go into the exercise area and, after two more glasses of orange cordial, Jane began to regain her composure.

"It looks like rain," I said, for want of something better to say.

"I suppose so," said Jane, still reluctant to speak.

Our conversation, if it could be described as such, was interrupted by the sound of thunder and within seconds it began to rain. I looked at Jane expecting her to move to the shelter of the police station but she remained motionless and neither of us spoke. One minute later the heavens opened and I dashed for the doorway. Jane stayed where she was, leaning against a wall and just staring down at the ground. She did not move and in no time at all she was soaking wet. Rainwater mixed with fresh tears as her body began to shake again and it was clear that the realisation of the enormity of what had happened had finally hit home. The rain stopped as quickly as it started and after a few minutes a policewoman took her gently by the arm and with a kindly word escorted her into the charge office. With her shoulders bowed and her hair hanging wet and limp, Jane seemed to have got smaller. She had become just a frightened young woman.

As the charge office door closed, I remember looking at the custody sergeant. More for want of something to say rather than an attempt to lighten the situation, he said that she would have a long time to dry out.

I suggested that they should leave her for a short time and asked them to ring her family to ask them to bring her a change of clothes. I waited in the police station for her parents to arrive.

Mr & Mrs Webb were a middle aged couple in their late fifties or early sixties.

I had not met them before and the first thing that struck me about them was their appearance. They didn't look like a couple. He was smartly dressed in cavalry twill trousers and a sports jacket with sleeves that had been intended for someone with longer arms. He was clean shaven and had obviously taken Henry Cooper's advice to 'splash on the Brut'.

Indeed, his face had all the hallmarks of a boxer, and he later told me that he was a retired steel worker and had had an impressive amateur boxing career. He had kept himself extremely fit and proudly boasted a thirty-four inch waist, something I hadn't had since I was twenty five.

Mrs Webb on the other hand had not worn as well. Her eyes were care worn and she looked much older than her fifty-five years. Alongside Mr Webb she was a rather insignificant figure with dowdy coloured clothes, covered by a worn out long brown mac. She carried a bulging shopping bag and trembled as I explained what had happened.

Mr Webb remained silent as I imparted my grim tidings and just stared at the floor, his lips quivering as if tears were near. His wife became distraught and he tried to console her, but it was a task he was not comfortable with.

Mrs Webb then took Jane's clothing out of her bag and I volunteered to take it into the cell area, where it was passed to Jane, who had been given the opportunity to take a shower and have a warm drink. She had refused any food and the untouched meal was left on the charge office counter where a number of officers had helped themselves to what looked to have been sausage and chips.

The detective inspector in charge of the enquiry, who was inappropriately named Meek, presented himself at the charge office desk and informed me that he was ready to commence the interview.

I returned to Jane's cell and assured myself that she was ready. She was clean and tidy and her hair, which had been washed, was combed backwards. Strands of hair had begun to stick out as they dried.

"I didn't mean to kill her Mr Smith," said Jane, "I honestly didn't realise that I had the glass in my hand. It was just an immediate reaction. I never intended this to happen."

The difficulty was that the blow which had inflicted the wound led to the girl's death. I believed that she was guilty of manslaughter but the problem that Jane had was to convince the detective inspector who, like many of his rank, had been there before and seen it all.

I left the cell and told him that Jane was ready for the interview, but first I asked his view as to what had happened.

"Mr Smith, you can't tell me that she did not intend to cause grievous bodily harm. I accept she might not have intended to kill, but I only have to prove that she intended to do GBH to establish murder."

"I don't think she did," I replied. "I think that it happened so quickly she didn't realise that she had got the glass in her hand."

"Bollocks," said the detective inspector.

Fortunately, I knew him well, otherwise I would have been less than impressed with his response.

"No, seriously," I said, "I think that she had been grossly effected by drink and her immediate reaction was to strike out. I have not seen any evidence that she broke the glass before using it. That rather tends to support her story doesn't it?"

We'll see," said the detective inspector, "We'll see." With that he strode into the interview room where Jane was already waiting.

His attitude changed the moment he entered the room. He smiled at Jane and asked if she would like a drink. This was all part and parcel of his act, of course, lulling his subject into a false sense of security before delivering the killer punch.

"Hello Jane," he began, "I'm Detective Inspector Meek and I have to interview you about this case. I will try to be brief and if you feel up to it I'd like to start now."

Before Jane could answer Detective Inspection Meek had started to write out the caution on the notes he would take contemporaneously. He was working on automatic pilot. Any second now, I thought, he will smile and say, "Now then Jane, tell us what happened," and lo and behold he did.

Jane related her story as best she could but there were parts of the tale which were confused and unclear. This is usually because the defendant does not want to remember or can't by reason of drink, drugs or trauma, or sometimes a mixture of them all.

As she spoke, her voice wavered, interrupted at times by sharp intakes of breath as she tried to keep her composure. Tears welled in her eyes from time to time as she explained how she had drunk twelve pints of lager and, as she put it, the odd brandy and Babycham. It was a lethal mixture which would be sufficient not only to remove her inhibitions but also to add the spark to her already volatile temper.

So many acts of violence are fuelled by alcohol that it cannot be regarded as mitigation at the end of the day, but perhaps it does give a reason why some people act out of character. Although Jane's case it could be said that she had acted 'in character'. She related how she had been dancing in the club when she saw the complainant, whose tongue had been loosened by drink making certain comments to her friends. Unfortunately, they were of an offensive nature and, while Jane could not hear the exact words, the girls' gesticulations were enough for her to recognise the general implications of what was being said.

As the evening progressed, Jane was subjected to more and more humiliation. At first she gave the impression that she was not aware of what was going on and even went to the other side of the dance floor, but the girl and her party followed her and the behaviour persisted.

She rebuked the girl on one occasion warning her that if she didn't stop pestering her she would 'bottle' her. This was to be one of the major points of the prosecution case which supported the claim that the assault was premeditated.

As the evening wore on, Jane began taking her beer glasses onto the dance floor. This was not normally allowed, but it was busy and the bouncers had not seen what was going on.

At approximately 1.45am when the delirium on the dance floor was at its height, the victim danced behind Jane and simulated thrusting motions with her hips. Unfortunately, Jane saw what was happening and in a split second, without any real thought, she swung her fist towards the girl's face.

There was no time to fend off the blow and unfortunately the glass in Jane's hand hit the girl's neck. Blood was everywhere as the blow damaged a main artery. As a result of the glass smashing on impact, the palm of Jane's hand was also cut quite badly.

It was some seconds before anyone made a move, but eventually the door staff were alerted and the crowd was moved back. An ambulance was called and within minutes the police had arrived.

Valiant attempts were made to stop the flow of blood, but by the time the girl had arrived at the hospital she was dead.

Jane had made no attempt to leave the scene and was led away by the police.

Detective Inspector Meek had listened intently, scribbling furiously to keep up with Jane's account of the incident, but the corner of his mouth twitched signalling a marked reluctance to accept what Jane was saying.

"Did you intent to kill her?" he asked with the gentility of a steam hammer.

"No," replied Jane, equally as forcefully.

Detective Inspector Meek persisted with his line of questioning for over an hour, but Jane stuck to her story, repeating that she had no intention of either killing the girl or indeed causing grievous bodily harm.

"You must have know you were holding a glass," persisted Detective Inspector Meek.

"Why?" asked Jane, with growing confidence.

"Because you were carrying it. If you hadn't known it you would have dropped it."

There was no reply.

"Well?"" said Meek, "Come on," he continued, "I can't spell silence.

Her inability to answer was as good as an admission.

"You see," said Meek, "I think you knew you had the glass and when you struck out you intended to injure the girl, which is just what happened. Why don't you admit it? Think of that poor girl's family. She was an only child. What about her poor parents? Can you image how they feel?"

71

The old 'heart strings routine' was the clue that the interview was coming to an end. The inspector's most valuable point was that if you hit someone with a glass, you have to expect that they will be seriously injured and all he had to prove was that there was either an intent to kill or to do grievous bodily harm.

Jane answered her questions well until we got to that point.

"Isn't it right Jane, that if you hit someone with a glass you can expect them to be badly injured?"

It was nearing the end of a long day and a very stressful interview, and I was considering whether the question was fair, when Jane answered,

"Yes, I suppose so."

I was alarmed, because Meek was talking her into admitting that she expected to cause grievous bodily harm. With this admission, his case was made out but, as I understood her case, she was saying that she didn't realise that she was holding the glass in the first place.

I interrupted and asked for this point to be clarified. Jane realised what was happening and she countered Meeks' questions.

"I know that if you hit somebody with a glass they will be badly injured, but that wasn't what happened here, because I didn't realise I had the glass."

This answer ruffled Meeks' feathers and he was clearly annoyed at my interruption, suggesting that I put the words into Jane's mouth. I pointed out that she had made this point earlier in the interview and I had merely attempted to clarify what she had already said.

"You were having a drink weren't you?" he continued.

"Yes," said Jane.

"Well, what were you drinking it out of?" said Meek, with a hint of annoyance in his voice.

"I suppose I was drinking it out of a glass," said Jane.

"Well, where was the glass?" said Meek.

"Well I suppose it was in my hand," she said.

"So you must have realised that you were holding it then?" said the officer.

Before I could interrupt again, Jane replied.

"No, I didn't, I'm just agreeing that if I had a glass and I was drinking from it then it would be in my hand."

"Well I put it to you that you must have known," said Meek.

"Well I suppose I must have known," Jane said.

I was in despair with her answer but Meek sensed victory.

"Well, there we are then, so you accept that you knew you had a glass in your hand at the time of the blow?"

"I don't know.   I don't know what's going on," said Jane. She then burst into tears.

I took the break in the proceedings to remind the officer of her earlier comments in relation to the glass and asked Jane to clarify the position once again, which she did quite adequately.

"But she has just accepted, Mr Smith, that she knew that she had the glass," said Meek.

"No she didn't," I replied.   "All she accepted was that if she had been drinking from a glass it would be obvious that she would be holding it.   That is far different from whether she realised that she was holding it at the time of the assault."

The next part of the interview was not to be so straightforward.   Meek continued.

"Do you remember when the girl was dancing, she was in a group?"

"No" said Jane thoughtfully.   "It happened so quickly I didn't notice who she was with because I wasn't paying any attention to her."

"Well we have a witness who says that she saw you move some five or six steps towards the girl before the assault took place. What do you say to that?"

"I can't remember that," said Jane, "All I can remember is turning round and seeing her doing or saying something and me just hitting out."

Meek continued undeterred, almost as if she had not made an answer to his question, as he read from the witness statement;

".......I saw the girl's face. She was looking aggressively at Shirley, so much so that I feared there would be trouble. I then saw her move some five or six paces towards Shirley and bring back her right hand. I saw that there was a glass in the hand, although I can't recall whether it had anything in it. She then pushed the glass into Shirley's face. I saw Shirley try to move out of the way, but the glass hit the side of her neck with such force that it smashed. My opinion of what I saw was that this had been done intentionally."

I was unhappy about her 'opinion', but Jane countered quite well.

"She is her best friend. She is bound to stick up for her. She will be angry with me because of what happened and so she will be trying to get me into trouble."

The witness statement was interesting because it said that she was one of a group of four friends which included the dead girl. Neither of the two other girls had given witness statements, a fact that I found suspicious.

Meek recapped the facts once again before concluding.

"I put it to you that if you did not intend to murder Shirley, then you intended to do her grievous bodily harm."

"Neither," said Jane defiantly.

"But we still get back to the same thing. If you hit somebody with a glass you must expect that you are going to do them a serious injury."

By this time Jane was well versed in her answer.

"I did not know that I had the glass. I did not intend to do her any serious injury and I was frightened when I saw that I had."

It was true that if she had lost her temper then it is highly likely that there would have been more than one blow. Meek on the other hand countered that by saying that the sight of all the blood would have rapidly brought her to her senses. But, as Meek pointed out as he concluded the interview, it would be a matter for the jury to decide upon.

Old habits die hard with seasoned CID officers and after the formal interview had finished he started 'chatting' to Jane, asking further questions. I immediately advised Jane not to answer as the conversation was not being recorded. Meek looked at me, shook his head, and said,

"Really, Mr Smith."

He said it as though I should have been ashamed of interfering, but unfortunately Meek was either unwilling or unable to accept that I had a job to do, and I was intent upon doing it to the best of my ability.

Meek then announced that he would be charging Jane with murder, a statement which induced a sharp intake of breath from Jane.

"Murder?" she said slowly.

"Yes, murder Miss Webb. I believe that you intended to kill the girl and, what's more, we intend to prove it."

With that Meek left the room slamming the door in the process. He walked down the corridor whistling the tune of 'Happy Birthday to you'.

I have always been disappointed with police officers who feel that solicitors interfere. They seem unable to accept that we have a job to do just like them. Many think that the solicitor is involved in some kind of plot to exculpate the defendant from liability.   I returned to the foyer of the police station to explain to Mr & Mrs Webb what was happening.   They were still in a state of shock and Mrs Webb's eye twitched violently as we spoke.

I explained the position as best I could and told them that it might be possible to see their daughter after she was charged. I went back into the charge office to find Jane already there with the sergeant who was reading her her rights.

She was charged with murder contrary to common law and asked if she had any comments to make.   Jane gulped and tried to speak but couldn't.   The sergeant waited but then wrote the words, "no reply" on the charge sheet and handed me a copy.

When the charging had been completed, Jane was taken away for photographs and fingerprints, and then onto her single cell where she was to remain until the following day when she would appear before the court.

Before I left the cell area, I paused and looked through the spy hole in the cell door.   I saw Jane with her head in her hands, weeping uncontrollably.

During this time a visit was arranged for Mr & Mrs Webb who were asked to wait in an interview room.   When Jane was brought in there was complete silence.   I left, closing the door, believing that it should be a moment of complete privacy for the three of them.

The unacceptability of untimely death had affected us all, but Jane's father in particular.   He walked head bowed from the interview room to the foyer and then out into the street.   I watched from the cell window to see a broken man being led by his wife.

I bumped into Meek as I left.

"Juries don't like dykes," said Detective Inspector Meek, "The odds are against her."   And then he had an afterthought,

"...She'll get on well in a women's prison, they'll like her!" Detective Inspector Meek whistled 'Strangers in the Night' as he set off for the tea room.

The court refused Jane's bail application, not only because she was facing a most serious charge, but because she had committed the alleged offence while on bail for the other matter. She was taken to HM Prison Risley, near Warrington which is an awful two hour drive, weaving in and out of lines of lorries which stop and start between the various road works on the M62. In all the years that I have travelled on the motorway, I cannot recall one trip free of roadworks.

The prison houses remands, who are people in custody pending trial or sentence. It is divided into two sections for male and female prisoners. The walk through the paved area from reception to the prison itself is known as the 'Valley of a Thousand Cuts,' as it is overlooked by the women's cells. Anyone walking through is subjected to a torrent of shouts and taunts which can either inflate your ego or destroy it absolutely.

Cries of 'get em off' and 'show us your arse' are common place and many of the requests and suggestions were interesting, but some quite frankly physically impossible.

The visits were held in a large room similar to a meeting hall, where small tables and tubular chairs were laid out in regimental rows. The earliest starting time was 9.15am and 'chuck out time' was 11.30am. It seemed a very long way to travel for only a two hour visit, but the afternoon session didn't start until after I had to get back.

The female warders were an interesting group, some of whom would have done very well against the American heavyweight boxing champion of the day Larry Holmes. One in particular used to greet me at the gates and take me to the special visits centre. She bore a marked resemblance to the wrestler Mick

77

McManus. In fact, but for the moustache, I would have thought that it was him.

Cigarettes were valuable items on the black market but drugs had not become as freely available as they would in later years.

Jane presented a very different picture in the prison setting. She had lost a great deal of weight and her face was a sickly colour. I also noticed that she was plagued with cold-sores, something which caused her considerable embarrassment.

We discussed the case over and over again in the weeks leading up to the trial and each interview ended in the same way, with Jane asking me for a prediction as to result. Each time my reply had to be the same; "I just don't know."

Chapter Five

JANE'S TRIAL AND THE CASE OF THE FALSE LEG

The following week saw the first day of Jane's case. Trials can be won or lost at this stage, because if the jury gets a bad impression of the defendant they are against him or her from the start.

I had advised Jane to sit quietly with her head bowed and not to interrupt the questions in any way, no matter how annoyed she became if some of the questions or answers caused her offence.

Eventually, the first witness was called. It was the deceased girl's best friend. She came into court and took the oath as though she was a stranger to criminal proceedings. She was smartly dressed and on first sight presented a good impression. She gave a good account of herself, but then Peter Baker our defence Counsel cross-examined her and decided to put in her record, meaning that he told the jury about her criminal convictions. This worked, and her evidence was discredited. I couldn't help thinking that the jury had taken the view that she had stretched the truth for reasons of revenge.

On the second day of the trial, I went to visit Jane in the cells but she was not there. I was informed by the prison staff that the night before she had cut her wrists, with the result that the case was adjourned for forty eight hours to enable her to recover and return to court.

I had cases in Rotherham and Barnsley that day but I had called upon my friend Peter Hollingworth, a solicitor from Barnsley, to deal with that case and I had got two colleagues in Rotherham to share the cases that I had there. I managed to telephone the office and get them to hold my cases back so that I could take them over again.

When I arrived my clients greeted me with such comments as, "Where's tha been?"

"I thought tha weren't comin'."

"You're supposed to be on a murder case in Sheffield," and just simply,

"Bollocks."

It was too complicated to explain, so I just told them that it was their lucky day and I would stay with them until their cases were finished.

I was looking forward to a free afternoon in the office to deal with paperwork when the charge office at Rotherham police station contacted me,

"Good afternoon Mr Smith," said sergeant Brown, "I thought that you were in a murder trial in Sheffield?"

"I was," I said, "But it's a long story.   What can I do for you?"

"Well we have two young men here in the police station requiring your services.   They have been arrested on suspicion of theft of.........."

The Sergeant's words tailed off to silence.

"Hello, hello Dave is that you, are you there?" I shouted.

"Yes," said Sergeant Brown contemplatively.   "I'm sorry about that, I was just reading the reasons for the arrest, which can't be right.   Just hold on a minute."   I heard him speak to a colleague.

"This can't be right Fred, can it?   Theft of a leg."

I heard Fred reply,

"Yes, it's true Sarge, it's as true as I am standing here, but I think that you should insert the word 'aluminium' before leg."

"What the bloody hell's gone off?" said the sergeant.

"These lads have stolen an aluminium leg."

"Do me a favour, stop pissing about. What's gone off?"

"They have......" and then the conversation stopped when the two officers moved away from the phone.

Dave eventually returned to the phone and told me that he would explain everything when I arrived at the police station. I checked my watch and decided to go straight away in the hope that I would be finished in time to get back for lunch at the Keys.

As I left the reception, I noticed a man making an appointment to see me. I didn't know him but he was on crutches, having only one leg, and I distinctly heard the words 'theft' and 'compensation' spoken in a strong eastern European accent. I did not have time to wait, so I scooted out of the office and was down at the police station within five minutes.

Owen and Desmond Gillis were two local ne're-do-wells who would do anything for a laugh. The day before they had excelled themselves, when they embarked upon a scheme suggested in a bet. Anatole Stosik was a Polish war veteran who settled in England after the war. As a young man he had lost his leg in action and recently the British Legion had been instrumental in getting him an aluminium leg to replace the old wooden one he had worn since the end of the war. It was a splendid piece of modern technology which when attached was noticeable by only the slightest limp, which would be accentuated during cold weather. Mr Stosik wore specially made trousers with press studs down the side of the left leg for ease of release.

He was famous with the children in the locality because when he was drunk, which was quite often, he would remove the leg and do Long John Silver impressions to the children's great amusement. In his later years, Anatole had become quite eccentric, something which claimed the attentions of local idiots who tended to make fun of him.

His main drinking day was Friday after he had collected his pension. He would go to the local British Legion, drink far more than was good for him and then sleep it off in the local park.

The Gillis brothers had been in the Legion that day and observed Mr Stosik drink himself into his usual stupor.

I do not know who suggested it, but the regulars agreed that if the Gillis brothers could steal Mr Stosik's leg and bring it back to the pub, they would all chip in and give them £10 each.

And so, Owen and Desmond followed the unfortunate Mr Stosik and waited until he lapsed into sleep on a park bench. They then systematically unpicked the studs along his left trouser leg and unstrapped the aluminium limb. They did so quite carefully so as not to disturb Mr Stosik. They then ran off with great glee to show off their prize to the crowd waiting in the pub.

They received their reward and after three renditions of 'I'm Jake the Peg', the crowd got bored and the landlord told the brothers that he didn't want stolen property on his premises and that they should find Mr Stosik and give him his leg back.

Meanwhile, back at the park, Mr Stosik was coming round from his siesta, the sleep having helped to sober him up somewhat. It was not until he actually stood up that he realised he was legless and for once it had nothing to do with his alcohol intake.

He immediately began hopping to the nearest police station, collecting an entourage of children who began hopping after him.

The Gillis brothers arrived back at the park hoping to be able to replace the leg before Mr Stosik woke up. When they saw that he had gone, whatever goodwill they might have had disappeared and they took the leg to the local scrap dealer who weighed it and gave them twenty pence to go away.

On his arrival at the police station Mr Stosik reported the theft and he was given a pair of crutches and his bus fare. On his way home he went to see a solicitor with a view to making a claim for compensation. The police had no trouble in finding the Gillis brothers because someone who had been the victim of an earlier prank of theirs had been at the Legion when they had walked in holding the leg aloft. He had informed the police and within the hour they had been arrested. After much hilarity during the interviews, admissions were made, charges were laid and bail was granted.

Fortunately, the scrap dealer had not done anything with the leg and the police were able to return it to it's grateful owner. When the case came to court the Gillis brothers were fined and ordered to pay compensation to Mr Stosik, who became something of a local celebrity when the Rotherham Advertiser reported the case and stressed the war record of the unfortunate victim of the crime. In fact, Anatoli Stosik was a 'legend' in his own lifetime. Within a week the case provided some light relief, except for Mr Stosik but the time spent at the police station put me behind schedule. I was cursing the fact when I arrived back at the office to find that a number of whinging clients had telephoned complaining about my absence. The next telephone call was even less welcome.

"Crown Court on line one," said Tracey.

"Oh f..., flipping heck," I replied and took the call. "Hello, General Dogsbody here. How can I inconvenience myself to suit your convenience?"

"Hello," came the reply.

"Oh hello, what can I do for you?"

"Oh hello, this is the Crown Court, your case of Jane Webb."

"Yes," I replied.

"It will continue at 2.15pm."

It was 1.30pm and the journey to Sheffield was at least thirty minutes.

"Oh brilliant," I said, "Thank you for all the notice, and how do you think I am going to get there on time, a helicopter perhaps?"

"That's your problem," came the reply, "I've given you the message and that's it. I suggest that you are on time. After all, it is a murder trial."

Before I could give forth a mixed range of expletives, the caller rang off.

"Bastards!" I announced under my breath and set off for Sheffield.

I arrived there with five minutes to spare, so I visited Jane in the holding cell beneath the court. She was a lonely and forlorn figure, dressed in a plain blue suit, her hair left untidy. Her face was pale and drawn and she had fresh bandages, stained in the centre with blood from the two self-inflicted wounds around her wrists.

"Why Jane?" I asked as considerately as possible.

"It's alright for you. You don't know what I'm going through. I can't face going to prison for life. I just can't." said Jane tearfully.

"But you don't know the result yet. You have a real chance of getting manslaughter," I replied forcefully.

"You don't understand," said Jane. "I killed someone........she's dead........it's my fault, it's my conscience. I just cannot live with that............"

The enormity of what had happened had finally struck her.

"I'm guilty, I know it now and so do you. I want to plead guilty."

"You can't do that," I replied almost indignantly. "We are half-way through the trial. You can't just throw it in now."

"I don't care what happens to me any more. How can I live with this, and in prison at that. I don't want to live any more," she said firmly.

"For God's sake, pull yourself together," I announced.

"For God's sake, you say. For God's sake - and what will God think of me? I am beyond that now. Will you please leave me alone."

I did my best to comfort her and for a moment I thought I had succeeded, but we were interrupted by a jailer who told us that the court was waiting. I returned to the courtroom and listened to the remaining witnesses. Matters were beginning to go our way and at the end of the prosecution case the counsel for the prosecution took our Counsel on one side. I knew something was in the air. I asked our Counsel what was going on, believing that they were considering whether to accept manslaughter.

I was advised not to mention anything to Jane in case it turned out to be a false hope, but I thought it might just keep her spirits up for the rest of the trial and so, not for the first time, I decided to act against advice and follow my instinct.

When I got downstairs to the cell, Jane was sat alone staring into space. There was no hint of recognition in her face and she did not acknowledge me in any way.

"Jane, I've got some news for you, the prosecution has.........Jane are you listening to me?" I asked.

Just then, as the jailer entered the cell, I saw that Jane was holding a Bible. A page was turned over at the corner, as a marker.

"Your parents are here Jane, you can have a visit if you wish, but you only have two minutes. The bus is here to take you back and the driver has another pick up."

Jane nodded an acceptance and turned and smiled at me. She held out her hand and I took it, gently shaking it in the process. It seemed for the first time she had found an inner peace, but I was troubled for I was unaware of the reasons for the sudden change in attitude.

Jane greeted her parents through the glass partition. None of them spoke. Mr Webb looked tired and ill, his face contorted with the pain he was in from an aggressive and unsympathetic ulcer. Mrs Webb on the other hand, was in tears.

Jane finally spoke.

"It's alright mother," she said. "I'm alright now. Everything is alright. I promise you don't need to worry any more. I will be fine where I am going......"

Her outstretched hand came into contact with the dividing screen as she pressed her palm against the glass. Her parents did the same. The moment was intense yet moving and it did not seem right to interrupt. That job was saved for the ubiquitous jailer who had done the job too long to be moved by such things.

For a second I hated him as he led Jane away.

"But Jane, I must tell you what is happening," I shouted after her, but before I could speak further she just mouthed the word 'Goodbye' and was led away.

"I've got to see her for a moment," I shouted through the door to the jailer.

"Tomorrow," came the reply, "It will wait."

"Ignorant bastard," I said under my breath as I listened through the door to the sound of the clinking of keys on the jailer's massive key ring which was large enough to lasso a small dog. It sounded rather like the clanking of chains in the distance.

"What's wrong with Jane?" asked her mother, "í have never seen her like that before. How strange she was."

"Don't worry," I said, "I'll see her first thing in the morning, I'm sure she will be OK."

The following morning I arrived at court earlier than usual to be told that the prosecution would be prepared, having considered the evidence which had been given in the trial, to accept a guilty plea to a charge of manslaughter, providing the judge agreed.

We had damaged the prosecution by showing that their witnesses were less than honest in their testimonies and running the trial further may put a manslaughter conviction at risk. It was probably best to guarantee something in the certain knowledge that we could not risk going on with the trial and stare a murder conviction firmly in the face.

I set off for the cells as quickly as I could, but I felt that something was wrong. I have often laid claim to a sixth sense where bad news was concerned, and this was to be no exception.

The jailer let me in and I went to Jane's cell, but she had not arrived.

"The bus hasn't come yet," said the jailer, "But they'll get here soon enough."

I sat on the wooden bench and perused the graffiti laden walls. The ceilings, formerly white, were brown with years of nicotine staining. The entire cell reeked of tobacco smoke and body odour, which vied for my attention with the drifting smell of fresh bacon being fried in the jailer's rest room.

It was then that I noticed a small Bible on the seat in the corner. I picked it up and saw the name written on the inside cover. It read:

"JANE WEBB - THRYBERGH COMPREHENSIVE 1975"

As I flicked through the pages, I came to one page with the corner folded over. The chapter was headed Exodus 22. Almost as if I knew where to look I read verse 24, which said: "Eye for eye, tooth for tooth, hand for hand and foot for foot." Before I could read any further, a white shirted lady prison officer walked into the cell doorway, blocking out the light such was her size.

"Are you Mr Smith?" she said in a low voice.

"Yes I am, what can I do for you?"

"Are you Jane Webb's solicitor?" she demanded.

"Yes," I replied, almost in the form of a question.

"I'm afraid I have bad news for you," she said, without altering the inflection in her voice.

"What's happened?" I asked...."It's Jane isn't it?" I said, knowing something had happened.

"Well I can tell you now because the court has already been informed. She's dead," she said, resisting the urge to tell me gently.

Despite the shock, I was able to ask what had happened.

"She used her pillowcase........tore it up and made a rope. We found her this morning. She must have done it after lights out. She was in a cell on her own...rule 43's protection. You know the one. The doctor said she had been dead for hours. There was no note or anything."

"No," I interrupted, "There wouldn't be."

"I'm sorry?" said the officer.

I didn't answer straight away, I was in a state of shock. I turned to leave, but the officer's words stopped my progress.

"Has she anything here.....any family or anything?"

"Er yes," I replied........... "Her parents."

"Who?" she asked again.

"Er......her parents," I said, "I'm sorry I'm a little shocked."

88

"Well she was just a client wasn't she? Tomorrow's another day. There's plenty of others....It's one less for the tax payer to pay for.........." she wandered off without waiting for my reply.

I couldn't think of anything suitable, certainly not without swearing, so I left to go into court.

In the foyer sat Jane's parents. They both stood up when I walked in. Mr Webb was holding his cap and Mrs Webb her handbag.

Detective Inspector Meek got to me first and I indicated that they should wait for me. Meek spoke in a serious tone.

"Have you heard?" he asked.

"Yes.......just...."

"Hanging wasn't it?"

"Yes," I replied, "Hanging."

"What about them?" asked Meek, referring to Jane's parents.

"They don't know yet."

I did not reply, but just looked across at them, attempting to return their smiles.

"Look," said Meek, "I'll tell them."

I took his arm.

"No, it's alright, I'll see them. I would prefer it came from me."

"OK," said Meek, "It's a shame, apparently the judge would have agreed to......"

I turned away before he could finish and walked over to Mr & Mrs Webb.

"Is everything OK Mr Smith?" asked Jane's father.

I did not answer and led them away to an interview room. I ushered them inside, changed the marker on the door from vacant to engaged and closed it. This was going to take sometime.

Chapter Six

AS FAR AS I AM CONCERNED, I AM THE EARL OF SCARBOROUGH

Working in the legal profession you certainly see life, and indeed all too frequently you see death. The famous saying 'but for fools and rogues' sits well at the profession's door which certainly has a constant queue of rogues waiting to be dealt with. But we must not forget the fools. Geoffrey Samuel Plowright was one such character. Many suggested that he was not so much a fool as stark raving mad, and was so far gone even the mental hospitals wouldn't take him. It was not possible to get two consultant psychiatrists to agree about him, which presented a problem because two such opinions are required before a hospital order can be made.

Geoffrey did not accept that he was mad and in fact the very suggestion that he was would send him into a wild frenzy calmed only by an injection and a big mallet.

Solicitors hold a fascination for loonies and so they are a regular feature of the appointment list, and tend to leave untold problems in their wake.

Some are harmless but others are not, and agencies who have to deal with them are perpetually on guard against sudden movements.

Geoffrey's condition worsened over the years I knew him, aggravated by tremendous mood swings and fits of depression. When he was acting normally he was perfectly reasonable, if slightly eccentric, but when the fancy took him he could be as irrational as it was possible to be. He was also six foot six inches tall and weighed eighteen stones, with a shiny bald head and dark piercing eyes. He was

Rasputinesque without the hair, accent and the ability to care for haemophiliacs.

One afternoon just in May 1983, I was in the midst of a massive appointment list when Geoffrey appeared at reception and frightened poor old Tracey by letting his eyes roll up into his head and pretending to be a Dalek.

"Is……he……in……please….. I…….need help they……..have tried to poison me……at the Cross Keys."

"Oh, you've had the steak and kidney pie then?" said the beleaguered Tracey in a reception swamped with weirdoes.

I led the Dalek into my office thinking that it was a good job we'd moved last year as Daleks can't manage stairs. I sat him down.

"Paraquat," said Geoffrey forcefully.

"Paraquat," I reported, equally as forcefully.

"Yes, Paraquat - in the beer, well, in my beer at least, and they did it."

Geoffrey sat back in his chair waiting for me to ask.

"They?"

"Yes," said Geoffrey banging his hand on the desk with unacceptable force.

"Yes, but we will get them, Montmorency," added Geoffrey.

I did not pursue the 'Montmorency' bit.

"I want to sue them, they want to get rid of me."

Geoffrey exhibited classic signs of a persecution complex more commonly known as paranoia.

"Why would anyone want to poison you Geoffrey?" I asked, trying to play the close friendship card.

"Because I am really the Earl of Scarborough!!!!!"

The revelation took me by surprise, so much so the only thing I could think of to say was that I had never met a real Earl before.

"I should be referred to as my liege," said Geoffrey.

91

"Very well……..my liege," I said, trying to humour him.
"Would you like a Woodbine?" I asked passing him a half empty cigarette packet.

"Earls don't smoke!" was the reply.

"Right," I said.

"I want you to act quickly," said Geoffrey, taking on an air of indifference.

"Report to me by the end of the week," and with that he took his leave, shouting "Paraquat" as he left reception.

I turned to a waiting client and announced,

"That was the Earl of Scarborough.   They are poisoning him."

"Good idea," said my old friend Jack, who was sat waiting to see me.

"What's his problem?" said Jack.

"Paranoid schizophrenia," I replied to a confused Jack, who knew even less about psychiatry than I did.

"He's a zit," said Jack.

"A what?" I asked.

"A zit," said Jack.   "Tha knows what that is dunt tha?"

"Of course," I replied in a state of complete confusion.

"Now what's to do Jack?"

"Nowt for me" said Jack.   "It's our 'orace tha sees.   He's gone and got nicked for pinching, but it weren't 'im. They've set im up tha knows, bastard coppers."

"Why, what's he supposed to have done?"

"Nicked all them jonnies from that lorry at Boots," said Jack knowingly.

I had long since realised that I needed a can opener to get information out of Jack.   He had the habit of giving me minor snippets of a story prompting me to uncover the rest by a process of elimination.

"What lorry?" I asked.

"That lorry wi deliveries on," said Jack, as if I should know the movements of every item of haulage in Rotherham.

"Wait a minute," I said, "I think I've got it…there is a delivery lorry which has taken its goods to Boots…yes?"

"Yes," repeated an eager Jack.

"While at the point of delivery someone has entered the lorry and stolen some of its contents."

"No," said Jack.

"No?" I asked. "Where have I gone wrong?"

"Not some of its contents," said Jack, as if he was privy to some great secret. "All of it!!"

"All of it?" I repeated.

"Yes, all of it, full bag o' mashings, the lot, maximum, all on it, everything, full monty……tha knows."

"Anything else?" I asked sarcastically.

"Argh," said Jack, nodding in approval.

"What Jack?"

"Container,"

"Container?" I replied.

"Argh," said Jack.

"You mean they have stolen the container as well?"

"Argh," said Jack…. "and the lorry that pulled it."

"You mean the lorry and its load has gone?" I asked in exasperation.

"Argh," said Jack, looking for other words to describe "all of it."

"Nowt left," said Jack.

"And your Horace is thought to be responsible?"

"Argh, but it weren't him," he said knowingly.

Just then there was a knocking on the door which interrupted the discussions.

"Come in," I shouted, but nothing happened.

I shouted louder.

"Come in."

Again no answer.

"Come in for God's sake!"

Again no answer.

I left my seat and went to the door.

I opened it but there was no-one there. By the time I got back to my seat the knocking started again.

I shot up and pulled the door open forcibly in my attempt to catch out the intruder.

As the door opened I saw a young lad wearing an ex-army combat jacket and a wide grin.

"Come in sergeant," I said, breathing a sigh as I noticed three stripes on the right arm. It was Albert.

Albert walked in. The jacket was ill-fitting, and his left arm appeared to have been demoted, as it bore only two stripes.

"You're only a corporal on that side then, Albert?"' I announced with a grin.

"Tha what?" said Albert.

"Oh nothing, it was just that you have three stripes on one arm and two on the other, " I ventured.

"That's how it was when I got it," said Albert, putting me firmly in my place without knowing it.

"Yes, well come in, sit down and keep quiet. Your dad's got a problem."

"Argh, me anall," said Albert, failing to show whether he was joking or not.

I returned to my conversation with Jack.

"I'll have to see your Horace before he is interviewed."

"Argh," said Jack, "Eell come in and see thee whenever tha wants him, soon though cos coppers want 'im tomorrow neet."

"OK Jack, I'll see him tomorrow at 5pm if that's OK."

94

Argh," said Jack, "That'll do reight. I'm off, come on Albert, let's geroff."

Albert was still smiling as if he had played some awful joke upon me and was waiting to see the result.

"By the way Jack, there was something. What did you say the lorry's load was?"

"Jonnies," said Jack.

"Jonnies?" I asked in confusion. "Jonnies what?"

"Tha knows, jonnies, " said Jack perplexed at my inability to comprehend what he thought was obvious.

"Jonnies….rubbers….sheaths….covers….skins…..catholic hats…..Oh for God's sake CONDOMS!"

"Condoms." I replied.

"Argh, condoms. 14,000 boxes apparently," said Jack with all the verve of a connoisseur.

I thought about what Jack had said.

I had visions of the Rotherham branch of Boots taking delivery of such an amount of rubber goods and my mind imagined row after row of people queuing outside the branch with a sign for all to see saying 'only one box per person'.

I had begun to realise that we must have been the condom centre of South Yorkshire, but my considerations were disturbed by Jack's explanation.

"They weren't all for Rotherham tha knows, there was more than wun shop to deliver to."

"Oh, that's alright then. So Rotherham is not the sex centre of the North?"

"Tha what?" asked jack.

"I wonder if the thief knew what the lorry was carrying?" I asked Jack.

"He certainly did when 'e gorit 'ome," said Jack.

"They would last quite a bit," I suggested.

"Argh," said Jack, "Tha could afford to wear three at a time."

We both laughed.

It then occurred to me that Jack's knowledge of the shipment and the quantities was suspicious to say the least.

I then remembered the last time Jack had acquired goods from a lorry. Cigars had been stolen at that time and my imagination ran wild with visions of court corridors and tea rooms full of men wearing stolen condoms.

"Bloody hell," I said. "Who would want to steal that lot," I asked.

"I don't think they knew what were in the lorry," said Jack.

"What were they after do you think?" I asked, beginning to realise that Jack had more than a supporting role in the venture.

"I think they were after scent and electrical stuff tha knows."

"Well they made a massive mistake this time, didn't they?" I suggested.

"Argh, they did. There's not much call for condoms around our end."

I wondered if Jack realised what he had said.

"Have you all been neutered?" I asked, but Jack did not get the joke.

I attempted another joke.

"I suppose the incidence of sexually transmitted diseases will be substantially reduced in your area now?"

"Dunt think so," said Jack in reply. "These condoms were only for men."

There was no hint of a smile about Jack's face, and I never found out what he was talking about.

"Why did the police pick on your Horace?" I asked, trying to get back to the job in question.

"They foun' 'em in his loft," said Jack thoughtfully.

"How may did they find?" I asked.

"All on em except wun box," said Jack.

"I suppose that the police concluded from that that Horace must have stolen them."

"'ow can they say that?" said Jack, "Just cos 'e got them in his loft, dunnt mean he nicked 'em."

"No, but it certainly puts your Horace firmly in the frame."

"Well I'm tellin thee, 'e ant dun it. Anyway 'e's a catholic."

"You don't mean to tell me that your Horace is religious?"" I asked in a rather accusatory fashion.

"He is where condoms are concerned, e's got five kids."

I'd almost given up, but I allowed myself one final comment.

"Wouldn't he be better off using the bloody things then?"

Jack smiled, and Albert burst out laughing. Both Jack and I stared at him with a rather questioning glance, for neither of us knew what was so funny.

"What's funny, our Albert?" asked Jack.

Albert answered immediately and said,

"Our 'orace………..a burglar?………….."

And with that Albert started to laugh again, leaving me in no doubt whatsoever that the family was mad.

"Why don't you get Horace to come in and see me and we will see if we can assist him."

"I'll do that Steve," said Jack, "Because our Albert is reight, 'orace does a lot of things but he is not a burglar or a lorry thief."

"I shouldn't imagine that he's got time," I suggested.

"Nay, he's not working, not since he got made redundant at the toilet roll factory."

I wasn't sure whether I dared to ask, but in the event I did,

"What did he do there?"

"He was a tester."

"A tester?"

"Argh," said Jack. "A tester."

I thought for a second or two and wondered whether I dare go any further, but curiosity had got the better of me.

"What does a tester do?" I asked.

I awaited his reply with baited breath, fear and trepidation. It just could not be what I was thinking.

"He used to test the rolls" said Jack.

"How?" I asked.

"He used to test the cardboard bit in the middle to make sure it was sealed, otherwise the rolls used to come to bits. Why, what did you think?" asked Jack, without any idea as to what had been in my mind.

I left the matter at that and we agreed that Jack would call later that week with his brother and I would see if I could sort out the problem.

I showed Jack out after giving Albert a clip round the ear for putting a little plastic duck in my fish tank. The manoeuvre caused Albert to start laughing again. As they left, I could hear the sound of a young man being slapped around the head. On returning to my room, I was in time to answer a telephone call from the local police station.

"Hello, Steve Smith speaking" I announced.

"Good afternoon Mr Smith, this is Sergeant Suter. I have a client of yours presently locked up demanding to see you before he is interviewed. If you could call down to see him it would help us, because he won't give us his real name."

"This sounds interesting sergeant, who does he say he is?"

I could hear the sergeant take a deep breath.

"He says he's Edwin, the Earl of Scarborough."

I joined in the joke and replied,

"What does the Earl of Scarborough want to see me for? Hasn't he got his own solicitor?"

I suspect the sergeant had missed the point, because he went on to explain that they did not believe he was who he claimed to be.

"He's not a big bald-headed bugger with wild eyes is he?" I asked.

"Yes, that's the one," said the sergeant. "He came into our reception causing trouble, demanding that we arrest everybody in the Cross Keys for poisoning him. He was asked to leave, but when he refused we had no option but to arrest him for breaching the peace. He has threatened to go back to the Cross Keys and poison them in return. In the circumstances, we just can't let him out in this state, although we are thinking about getting a psychiatrist to come and see if he is suitable for a section."

The words 'suitable for a section' is what happens to someone who is mentally ill when a consultant psychiatrist believes that he is unfit to remain at liberty. The usual result is that they are taken to the local hospital and placed in the psychiatric wing where they are drugged and monitored for a period of twenty eight days.

"Don't tell him that you are bringing a psychiatrist just yet. Let me put that to him when I come to the station."

When I got there, I was greeted by the care worn sergeant, who was working the last eighteen months of his contract before taking a well-earned retirement on a lump sum and reasonable pension. He had seen it all and nothing could surprise or shock him. He had been party to the worst that human nature had to offer leaving him with rather a sour disposition.

He called a young constable to go to Lord Scarborough's cell and bring him to be interviewed.

"Would you be kind enough, officer, to fetch My Lord the Earl of Scarborough so that his solicitor and confidant Mr

Smith can have the opportunity of discussing his present legal problem."

"Which cell is he in Sarge?" said the young fresh faced policeman, who appeared to have just started shaving.

"I will look at my board," said the sergeant as he turned to see his small blackboard showing the cell occupancy. He looked to cell four which had the word 'Looney' at the side of it. Within seconds, the recipient of this rather discourteous title was brought out of his cell and, the sergeant bowed low before he spoke.

"My Lord, Mr Smith has arrived to see you. Mr Smith, I have pleasure in introducing to you My Lord the Earl of Scarborough."

It was almost as if Geoffrey had entered into the spirit of the banter, because he thanked the sergeant most graciously before speaking to me,

"After you Smith, I wish to speak with you in private."

I made my way to a small interview room on the corridor near to the charge office and once inside, I saw a small wooden desk which had a number of magazines scattered upon it. There was not one magazine under three years old.

I picked one up, turned to Geoffrey and simply said,

"I see Ghandi's dead."

"Ghandi who?" asked Geoffrey, and I decided not to confuse him further than he already was.

I planned to break it gently to Geoffrey that a psychiatrist had been requested, but I must confess that I had lost my bottle.

I tried to approach the issue from a different stand point.

"How are you feeling My Lord?"

"Perfectly well," said Geoffrey.

"You don't look very well to me My Lord, in fact you look really under the weather."

"Do I really?" said the Earl, "Now you come to mention it, I don't feel too well."

"A man of your position should have an examination by a doctor, whether the police like it or not."

My forceful attitude of concern about the Earl's welfare struck a cord. I continued.

"I don't care whether the police will be inconvenienced or not, I will demand that you be seen by a doctor. We will not be put off."

"Quite right," said the Earl. "Yes we will demand it. In fact I will speak to the sergeant myself."

He stood up, walked out of the interview room and approached the sergeant, who looked on with dismay.

"I demand to see a doctor."

"Certainly, My Lord," said the sergeant, "I'll deal with it straight away."

I chipped in.

"I'm not bothered what sort of doctor it is, providing it's not a vet, and we wish one to be called straight away."

The sergeant entered into the spirit of the ruse.

"Does that mean any doctor at all Mr Smith?"

"Any doctor at all, " I said, "Other than keep My Lord waiting."

"Quite right," said the Earl, who promptly walked back to the interview room. I winked at the sergeant and he returned the compliment as the Earl and I went off to read the old jokes from the Readers Digest magazines.

The hospital had a psychiatrist who was on call and was in the area, and within thirty minutes he was at the police station interviewing Geoffrey. Fifteen minutes later, the sergeant and I were to be most disappointed when the psychiatrist made his report.

"There's nothing wrong with him," he said. "It's true he is slightly eccentric, but I don't think that there is an ounce of aggression in him." With that we could hear the sound of shouting and smashing up of such furniture as there was in the cell.

I made my apologies and left, only to be contacted about an hour later to say that the gentle giant who was not a risk or a problem to anybody had involved himself in an attack upon three police officers and a police dog. Geoffrey was charged with assaulting all three officers and a most curious charge of criminal damage. The details of the damage were:

'That you caused criminal damage in that you did bite one police dog called Sherlock, causing damage to the said dog'.

Geoffrey was to be detained until the following day when I would have to make a bail application before the local magistrates.

When I appeared at court the following morning, I had a number of cases in addition to Geoffrey's. The courts always attempted to deal with the prisoners first, and that day was to be no exception. I explained the difficulty I had with Geoffrey to Keith Copley, the clerk of the court and I also explained that he would not answer to his real name. I pointed out that if the court persisted in calling him Geoffrey Plowright he would react by causing trouble in the dock and we would get nowhere. Keith entered into the spirit of things and with consummate diplomacy he dealt with his Lordship masterfully.

"Are you Geoffrey Samuel Plowright..........."

Keith paused as if embarrassed before continuing......

".....Otherwise known as the Earl of Scarborough?"

"I am Lord Scarborough, what of it?" said Geoffrey in arrogant defiance.

Keith read out the charges.

102

"It is said that you Geoffrey ...."

Copley paused before speaking further in a lower tone and looking from side to side as if guilty of some misdemeanour.

..."The Earl of Scarborough did on the fourth day of December assault P C Calladine in the execution of his duty contrary to section 51 of the Police Act 1954. Are you guilty or not guilty?"

"How dare you," shouted The Earl.

I then rose to my feet.

"May it please your worships, this is my application for an adjournment. I am seeking an extension of legal aid to facilitate the preparation of a report."

"What sort of report," said the chairman of the bench.

"A report as to fitness to plead Sir," I replied, not wanting to upset the Earl. Fortunately the chairman took the point and realised I had a very difficult situation on my hands.

The adjournment was granted but not before we were subjected to another outburst from an enraged Earl who was beginning to feel rather left out of the proceedings.

"Take me to the toilet," demanded Geoffrey.

"Take him down," said the chairman and with that Geoffrey was whisked away by three of the largest and heaviest constables in the South Yorkshire Police.

Just at that moment the emphasemic usher passed me note. It read:

'New client in the cells, Horace Heptonstall, charged with burglary."

Almost at the same time as I received the message, Jack appeared at the court room door gesticulating vigorously.

"What happened last night?" I asked. "I was there but no Horace."

"Sorry about that Steve," said Jack, "He buggered off, no-one knew where. Then this morning a little bird told me he was locked up, so I came 'ere."

"Why didn't he contact me?" I said with some surprise.

"You know our 'Orace, he wouldn't want to bother you at neet."

This was one of the nicest qualities of this family. Despite their peculiarities   they simply didn't want to be a nuisance outside business hours. Brilliant!

I left Jack to go to the cells, and armed with my notebook, legal aid forms and a bread and dripping sandwich courtesy of Jack, I went to see Horace.

He was sitting in cell number two. It was an awful place with an iron bed, a broken toilet and enough graffiti to keep you reading for a full day. The most infamous of guests had previously occupied cell two and now it housed Horace, a nice lad but not the brightest member of Jack's family.

"Now then Horace!" I said as he greeted me in his cell.

"Aye up," said Horace, "Can you get me bail? Only I 'ave 'ad nowt to eat and I think I've got summat."

This meant that Horace was desirous of bail and his incarceration had brought about an acute condition known colloquially as the shits.

"I've got my work cut out Horace," I said, "But with a bit of luck we should get you conditional bail."

"Fucking 'ell," protested Horace, "It's only a few fucking jonnies."

"No," I replied firmly, "It's a bit more than that. It's a trailer load and you have been found with them. Not to put too fine a point on it you have to explain why you have such stolen material in your possession so soon after the burglary. It is called the doctrine of recent possession.

"Tha' what?" said Horace.

"Well," I said, "It's difficult to explain, but you had the bent gear very soon after the burglary, so the suggestion is you have something to do with the burglary itself."

"Bollocks," said Horace, "It means fuck all."

"Well, not quite," I replied, "I can understand your concerns but please be assured they do have a case."

"Argh," said Horace, "But I dunt use 'em."

I believed him as he was the father of five children one born every year since his marriage. I did not need to be convinced.

"I'll 'ave 'andling," said Horace.

"Quite so," I replied. I think you have little alternative but what on earth did you get involved for?"

"I thought it were electrical gear like," said Horace.

"Why?" I asked.

"It's what we thought it were," replied Horace.

"What do you mean, we?" I asked.

I had touched a nerve and with that he 'shut up shop'.

I took instructions as quickly as possible and walked to court number one where Keith Copley the court clerk was waiting for me with Fred Jukes, the prosecutor.

I asked if the prosecutor was opposing bail and sure enough he was.

"Why?" I asked, "He has no current convictions, he is not on bail and his father will drive me mad if he is not let out."

"The police want a remand," said Fred.

"Why?" I asked, "On what basis? I'll bet it was because he's denied it," I pronounced.

"The police want a local remand," said Fred. "They think he's been bang at it and want to interview him further. They suspect that he has committed other offences.

"Bloody marvellous," I said, "What do I tell his father?"

"Tell him his son is being locked up," said Fred.

"You tell him," I replied, and Fred coughed. He was an experienced prosecutor with 'a lot of wool on his back' and he certainly didn't fancy a new nose job.

"I cannot see how you can justify a remand?" I demanded, but Fred was intransigent.

"Let's see what the court says," he replied.

"Thank you Fred," I announced in annoyance, knowing that Fred would get his 'local remand.'

I believe that magistrates are most reluctant to grant bail in such circumstances for fear that they might be letting a guilty man get away with it. I was proved right and Horace was remanded to the local cells for three days. It meant disappointment for him and his father and also for me, as I was unable to secure the freedom of one of my best clients.

In the event, the police and the magistrates were right for during the remand Horace admitted twelve other offences of shop burglary, involving many thousands of pounds worth of property.

On Horace's return to the court, Fred was again the prosecutor.

"We do not object to conditional bail." said Fred, "Providing he agrees a condition of residence, curfew between 8pm and 8am, reporting to the police station each day at 6pm and he stops burgling local shops.

"If you put it that way Fred," I announced, "I agree.

"Right," said Fred, "But if he offends on bail, he's for it!"

I couldn't argue with that and indeed I didn't. Horace was bailed, Jack was happy and at least all was well for the time being.

I spoke with Jack outside the court.

"He appears to have admitted lots of offences," I ventured.

"Argh," said Jack, "But he's only covering up for some bugger else."

"And who might that be Jack," I asked.

Jack shrugged his shoulders in an acceptance that he knew exactly who else was involved, but I did not press the point.

We shook hands and Jack left with Albert bringing up the rear. I realised that the family loyalty was strong even to the point of taking the blame for one of the other members wrong-doings. It was a curious proposition. On the one hand the majority of criminals spend their time blaming their responsibilities onto others, but Jack's family were a one off.

On the Sunday afternoon I answered a telephone call to find that my day would be ruined by a call out to the police station. I had two clients subject to detention. My Lord the Earl of Scarborough and McIver, otherwise known as Spider. Geoffrey, the Earl, had fallen out with his next door neighbour and had hit him repeatedly around the head with a frying pan. Spider on the other hand had been caught with £1,000 worth of heroin. The two cases could not have been more diverse.

I arrived at the police station and saw two other men injured and battle worn. They had been fighting outside a town centre public house and seemed hell bent on doing it all again in the charge office. A woman was being booked in on prostitution allegations and then there was the Earl! When the 'customers' had been shown to their 'rooms' the custody sergeant greeted me with his customary charm.

"Two beauties for you today, Mr Smith."

"Looks like it," I replied. "Who is Mr Plowright today, the Earl of Scarborough, Napoleon or a representative of MI5?"

"He has given his name," said the sergeant, "As Mr S D Smith, solicitor of Rotherham."

He looked at me with raised eyebrows as if to say "Sort that one out pal."

I looked at him with my eyebrows raised as if to say, "Fuck off!"

107

Geoffrey was sitting in his cell staring at the wall. He was quiet and contemplative. This worried me and I did not know from what direction he was going to come from.

"Hello Geoffrey," were my first words.

"I've told them I'm you," said Geoffrey boldly.

"Ah," I said, smiling as if he was paying me a compliment.

He laughed so I laughed. He laughed some more and so did I.

"What the hell were we laughing at," I thought to myself.

"What the hell are you laughing at?" asked Geoffrey earnestly.

"Same as you," I replied as quick as a flash.

Geoffrey laughed again and so did I. It had the potential of being the funniest interview ever.

"You know what?" Geoffrey said thoughtfully.

"No," I replied equally as thoughtfully. "What?"

"I think the system has it in for me. I think they will get me in the end."

"Do you really think so?" I asked, trying to humour him.

"Yes," he replied, "I really do.

For the first time I saw Geoffrey in a different light. He was actually very vulnerable as well as stark staring mad and I couldn't understand why nothing could be done. I did try but Geoffrey was an unusual case because he was not always mad.

I was convinced however that Armley jail was no place for him. The reaction from a room full of jailbirds to the cries of "Hello, I'm the Earl of Scarborough" left little to the imagination. In short, the poor bugger while big and strong, would be no match for any group and especially those well versed in the arts of tribal warfare.

The following day my pleas for bail fell on stoney ground. In fairness to the court, they could do little else than to remand him in custody. The over burdened and under-funded Health Service had nowhere to put him. He had offended while on bail and with serious offences too so it was a safe bet that if he had been bailed he would be back.

I wrote to the governor of the prison expressing my concerns only to find that Geoffrey had been transferred elsewhere owing to 'certain problems' he had been causing on the wing. Perhaps it was the knighthood he had bestowed upon one of the inmates. It wasn't so much the title more the placing of the sword on his shoulder which had caused the problem.

About three weeks later I saw Geoffrey in town carrying a plastic bag full of shopping. He appeared to be talking to himself and the sight of this large man with a bald head, wearing an ill-fitting suit afforded a great deal of amusement to passers-by. I stopped to speak to him but he continued walking, almost as if he had not seen me.

In the afternoon I was attending at court with a client who was answering to a warrant which had been issued for his arrest owing to his failure to attend court. We called to see the warrants officer to obtain all the paperwork we needed. On the top of the pile of warrants on his desk, I couldn't help but notice one bearing the name Geoffrey Samuel Plowright. It seems that Geoffrey had been prosecuted for breaching his probation order and failing to comply with it's requirements.

I told the warrants officer that Geoffrey was one of my clients and I offered to intercede on his behalf to see if I could try to avoid him being arrested by somehow persuading him to attend court. The warrants officer told me that after a reasonable start to his probation order, Geoffrey simply failed to turn up. In addition, he had not been calling to see his psychiatrist to answer his appointments, and neither had he taken any of his medication.

I wrote a letter to Geoffrey inviting him to call to see me, or at least contact me to discuss the position, but I never received a reply. I contacted the local DSS but found that he had not been signing on either. There appeared to be little that I could do and so I sent another letter in the hope that it might prompt him to contact me, but unfortunately this did not work either.

I forgot about Geoffrey until three weeks later when I opened the Rotherham Star newspaper. A headline screamed from the page: 'Local Man Found Hanged in his Home'.

My eyes were drawn to the report and there I found Geoffrey's name. He had committed suicide and his body had been found when police went to the house to execute the warrant for his arrest. The report said that the pathologist believed that Geoffrey had been dead for about three weeks.

I discovered that there had been a suicide note in which Geoffrey had indicated that 'they', whoever 'they' were, had got him in the end. He had signed it by using his own name, and there was no reference to the Earl of Scarborough.

I was more than willing to accept some of the blame for his death.

Chapter Seven

GARY'S BROTHER'S DEAF

The case of Gary Wilkes troubled me more than most. During my career I have often been disappointed with the court's decisions but this is not unusual if you care about what you are doing.   The advocates job is to represent the defendant and not to make the decisions, but in this case the truth was well hidden by the one person you would have thought would have wanted the truth to come out.

Gary Wilkes was a young man in his mid-twenties who could look after himself.   He was just over six feet tall with a broad athletic build.   His strong, pointed facial features were complemented with very dark eyes and a mass of curly jet black hair which almost gave him the appearance of a gypsy. If he had any particular facial characteristic, it would be his large ears with long lobes, one of which was lower than the other.

His younger brother Richie was about the same height but with a smaller wiry build.   From his appearance, there was no doubt that he and Gary were brothers and it was clear that ears ran in the family.

Gary was devoted to Richie, who sadly had been deaf since birth, and Gary had always 'looked after' his younger brother. As Richie grew up, his disability often led to misunderstandings and frustration which would manifest themselves in outbursts of temper.

His family were used to his disability and treated him no differently from anyone else, forgetting or perhaps overlooking the problem which haunted his existence.   It was never more poignant than when on his twenty-first birthday he broke down in tears when he could not hear his friends singing the birthday song. It was at times such as these when Richie's disability was never more apparent. However, to outsiders he was known to have a very short fuse.

On April Fools Day 1983, Gary had taken Richie for one of their regular outings to the local pub for a drink and a game of pool. The "Tap 'Ole" was the room with the pool table and dart board which was generally frequented by the younger male clientele. The day was no different from any other except that there was a stranger in the bar whose appearance made him stand out from the regulars. He was a thick set lad with a very short 'skinhead' haircut. He wore a denim shirt, jeans and large Doc Martin boots. Gary could remember thinking that he looked dead handy.

The afternoon session proceeded without incident until about 3pm when Gary and Richie were playing a game. The skinhead appeared to become impatient to play and at one point he slammed his twenty pence down on the side of the pool table just as Richie was preparing to take a shot. Gary and Richie had some difficulty playing the final ball resulting in them laughing and joking about each others ability to play. This angered the skinhead even more, to the extent that he stood at the head of the table tapping his foot. Finally, the black ball was potted, much to Richie's joy.

"About time," said the skinhead forcefully, "You want to learn to play properly."

Richie, who had his back to the skinhead, made no reply, for obvious reasons, and this seemed to cause even further annoyance.

"Are you fucking deaf as well as fucking hopeless?" shouted the skinhead.

At this stage Gary intervened,

112

"He is deaf, as a matter of fact, so leave him alone. He's not done anything to you. We don't want trouble. If you want the table, here it is."

"Right, bastard," said the skinhead, "I'm fucking sick of you. Outside, we'll sort this out, out there."

"Look," said Gary, "We don't want any trouble, you've got the table, start playing and leave us alone."

With that, the skinhead grabbed Gary and pushed him out of the door, through which Richie ran out after them. By the time Archie the landlord went outside, the skinhead was on the floor with blood coming out of his mouth and ear. An ambulance was called, and with it came the Rotherham police. The skinhead went away in the ambulance and Gary and Richie, who were the only ones who knew what had happened were told to wait in the pub so that the CID could speak with them. Within half an hour Gary and Richie were at the police station.

In those days, most defendants were interviewed by the police on their own. It was the Police and Criminal Evidence Act 1984 that prompted interviews to take place in the presence of a solicitor.

On the day of the incident, Gary was the only one of the three participants interviewed. He admitted hitting the skinhead and rendering him unconscious, saying that he had struck out in self-defence and that Richie had nothing at all to do with the incident.

The police were unable to interview Richie without an interpreter and so he was allowed to go home after a meeting was fixed for a later date. The skinhead was also unable to be interviewed as he was still unconscious.

The interview confirmed Gary's story that he had been pushed outside, whereupon he had hit out with one blow, resulting in the skinhead hitting the floor, banging his head and in the process suffering a fracture to his jaw.

Indeed, when he did recover, a statement was taken, but the skinhead had no recollection of what had occurred, as he claimed he was suffering from some form of post incident trauma which resulted in amnesia. He could remember going into the public house, but little else. Amnesia of this type is fairly common in assault cases where head injuries are sustained, but it can also be a convenient vehicle to hide the truth.

Gary came to see me just before his first court appearance,

"I want to plead not guilty because I was defending myself. I had no alternative but to hit him," said Gary, with the air of a man who had been well rehearsed.

I did not go into great detail at that stage because I did not have the prosecution evidence and I wanted to be sure of the case we had to defend.

Based upon what he told me, I thought Gary had a reasonable case. After all it seemed that we were dealing with a yob who had just got more than he had bargained for. I believed Gary and it's always more helpful if you are in a position so to do. Gary had given me the names of three witnesses who would all testify as to the yob's behaviour in the pub, but unfortunately I had no one who could give evidence as to the incident outside except, of course, Gary himself.

The prosecution had served their evidence upon me, which took the form of statements from the complainant, one lady witness who was standing at the bus stop nearby when the incident took place, and the two police officers who interviewed Gary. Gary had said one or two things in his interview which gave the impression that he had used a little more force than was appropriate for self-defence to apply.

114

I looked through the statements and saw that the yob had claimed he had been attacked without provocation. He had said that all he did was to join the queue by putting his money on the pool table. The money was pushed off the table by Richie and when the yob remonstrated with them he was dragged outside and beaten up.

We were able to counter all the allegations in the pub, although it was the incident outside which was the basis of the charge.

The lady at the bus stop was a little more tricky to deal with, because she said in her statement that she saw three men arguing outside the public house when one man set about a skinhead youth, hitting him repeatedly about the face and head. The interesting thing about her evidence was that she could not give a clear description of the attacker. I knew that she would be the major stumbling block of our defence, because she seemed to be clear about the fact that it was the skinhead who was attacked and not the other way around. I knew that if we could damage this evidence, we were in with a very good chance of an acquittal.

In the interview with the police, Gary had said, among other things,

"He attacked me so I hit him."

He then went on to say that he hit a further two blows to the face. That final comment worried me because the defence of self-defence is specific and says that you are only entitled to use a proportional amount of force to that which is used against you. It might seem like splitting hairs, but clearly there came a time when the skinhead's attack ceased and Gary then hit him again, at which time it could not be said that he was still defending himself. In those circumstances, a plea of self-defence might fail.

I have always thought that the rules surrounding self defence were a little unfair, in that someone can act as badly as he wants, and indeed commit a criminal act, but he still has the right of protection under the queen's peace. It seems odd to me that the people who are determined to break the law are then entitled to seek its protection when they get more than they bargained for. In my experience, I have never come across a case of a man who went out deliberately looking for a fight, won, and then went to report himself to the police.

The police did not ask Gary to explain why he continued to strike out and I felt that this left the door open for Gary to say that he had anticipated a further attack. This would make such action quite permissible. The law does not require you to be attacked before you take action. We certainly had an argument and I believed that if the yob could be shown for what he was, we had a reasonable chance in front of a fair bench.

However, the evidence of the lady witness intrigued me and I began to suspect that there was a little more to this incident than I had at first thought.

Systematically, I interviewed our three witnesses, all or whom were perfectly reputable and would have had no reason to lie. The first was the barmaid who was working in the pub on the day in question.

She was rather sympathetic to our cause, as it seemed that the yob had been rude to her prior to the incident with Gary. The second witness was a lad who was also waiting his turn to play pool and, while he was a friend of Gary and Richie's, he was of perfectly good character and made it quite plain that in his view the yob was out looking for trouble. The third witness was probably our key card because he was a man in his sixties who was a regular at the pub and was seated at the bar throughout the whole incident. He gave almost identical evidence to the other two witnesses. There were one or two areas of dispute, but only the sort you would expect honest witnesses to have. Indeed, I have always been very suspicious of witnesses who come and tell exactly the same story. They are often too well rehearsed to be totally truthful. I had wanted to interview Gary's brother but there were difficulties because he was deaf and I was unable to use sign language. I offered to arrange an interpreter, but Gary showed a marked reluctance to involve his brother in any way.

"But Gary, if you call Richie, his evidence may be helpful," I stressed.

"But he can't hear and he will be really embarrassed if he's got to perform sign language in front of a room full of people he doesn't know," replied Gary.

"But he must be used to communicating in that fashion and I can't see how he would be embarrassed, particularly if he knew he was helping his brother," I retorted.

"No, I've made up my mind," said Gary, "I don't want him involved. He will only get upset and when he does he......"

"He what?" I asked,

"He gets upset, that's all, and I don't want to put him through it. My mind's made up and that's it. We have got the three other witnesses and that should be enough, shouldn't it?" he asked, looking for my agreement.

"The problem with your witnesses is that they only saw the incident inside. Your charge surrounds the incident outside and on that we don't have any witnesses at all and that is why I want to call Richie."

"No, I'm sorry," said Gary, who then sat back in his chair with his arms folded, rather like the little boy who wants to take his ball away from the football match because he is not winning.

"Look, Gary, it's your case and you can run it how you want, but I have to advise you that I am not prepared to accept any responsibility for running the case without the main witness. If you get convicted it will be your fault and not mine."

"I'll accept that," said Gary, and with that I reluctantly drew the conversation to a close.

The trial had been set for a full day and when I arrived at court I found that the case would be heard by a visiting stipendiary magistrate. Not all magistrates are the same. They fall into two classifications. On the one hand there are the magistrates who are not legally qualified, who usually sit as a panel of three and are advised on the law by the clerk to the court and on the other hand there is the stipendiary magistrate who is an officer of the court, who is a qualified solicitor or barrister of standing. He usually sits alone and as a qualified lawyer makes all those decisions himself. It is often suggested that your chances of success in a trial are much less in front of a stipendiary. I found that if there may be a charitable vote or lay magistrates believe that it would be immoral to convict, they will dismiss a case if they feel it is right so to do. However, stipendiaries are not so helpful to the defence. This is one of the many reasons why I am so much in favour of lay magistrates. However, on this occasion the news as to the tribunal really dampened my enthusiasm. When we went into court, all the preliminaries were being dealt with and my client leaned across to me and whispered that he had been sentenced by the visiting stipendiary some two years before for something else. I doubted if the stipendiary would have remembered, because they deal with so many cases in a week let alone a period of two years, but I was honour bound to mention the matter to him. I am sure that it would not have made one jot of difference, but justice must be seen to be done and the stipendiary should make his own decision as to

118

whether he would retire gracefully or not.   In the event, he was a deputy stipendiary who was looking for a full-time appointment.   He did not wish to blot his copy book in any way and so, erring on the side of caution, he disqualified himself from dealing with the trial.

A fresh bench of magistrates was therefore drafted in from another court.   The chairman glowered at me as he entered the courtroom.   This perplexed me because I had always thought I got on very well with him.

The clerk then told me that the chairman had a council meeting at 2.30pm and he had not been prepared to miss it. In fairness, he had only expected to sit until 1pm, and so the thought of dealing with an all day trial got so far up his nose that it waved at me from the parting in his hair.

I tried to redeem the situation by expressing my regret that the bench had been placed in the unfortunate position of having to deal with a trial.   The Crown Prosecution Service man, my old friend Neil Franklin, sent me a little note with the words "F.......g creep" written on it, before standing and agreeing with my remarks.   I sent him a note back saying "You're an even bigger f.......g creep."

The chairman grunted in disapproval as my client was called back into court.   Gary repeated his plea of not guilty, and the reaction from the chairman was one of complete shock as though he had absolutely no idea that a trial was to take place. I suspect that he was showing his displeasure for my benefit, and indeed it worked.

I was beginning to wish that I had stayed with the stipendiary, when the complainant came in to give evidence.   His head was bald apart from perhaps a centimetre growth of hair. Neil Franklin, my opposite number, was an extremely experienced prosecutor and now enjoys high office in the South of England.   He knew that my trump card was to rely on the fact that the complainant was a skinhead and push home the suggestion that all such people were yobs. Of course, that is not true at all, because as fashions change, hairstyles change and all manner of people now adopt that particular hairstyle, but in the early eighties that look signalled Yob.

He read the oath as though the handling of a Bible was the most onerous task he had every performed, and the case began.

"Are you Kenneth Chambers?" asked Franklin.

"Argh," replied the yob with an attitude of "So what?"

"Nice start," I thought to myself. I looked across at the yob and he returned a challenging stare. How I wanted to say, "Yes lad, you've got it to come!" but I didn't.

He recounted his story faithfully according to his statement, but all the time he viewed me across the oak panelled courtroom with great suspicion. Franklin did his job to the letter, although I suspect he could find little favour for his witness.

It was then my turn to cross-examine. As I rose to my feet, we stared at each other as pugilists do before the bell of the opening round.

It was clear he viewed me as a representative of authority and as such had no respect whatsoever. The feeling was mutual. I decided not to mince my words.

"You are a skinhead are you not?" I asked fearlessly.

"It depends what you mean by skinhead," came the most capable answer.

Round one to the yob.

Just then the chairman, still blaming me for the trial, interrupted,

"Just what do you mean by skinhead Mr Smith. What is your version of a skinhead?"

120

I must say I was rather annoyed that the chairman was being seen to defend the witness, but I had just the answer.

"My view of a skinhead your worship, is a youth with his hair cut almost down to the wood!!"

The chairman could not conceal a smile. Round two to me and I continued my pursuit,

"A skinhead is a yob who believes that violence and disorder are acceptable codes of behaviour, yes?" I asked forcefully.

"Not at all," came the reply, "You can't generalise. Most solicitors are money grabbers oblivious to the dictates of society or its members, particularly the ones who are not fortunate enough to be in the same class."

The chairman removed his glasses and stared first at the yob and then at me. I knew what he was thinking, "Round three to Karl Marx." This was going to be a battle of wills.

"I don't give up easily you little shit," I said to myself. The effrontery of the youth was quite impressive, so I tried to move from a discussion on 'yob' philosophy to a more direct approach.

"You were looking for trouble?"

"No," came the reply.

"You were quite happy to cause a fight if necessary?"

"No."

"You were indiscriminate so far as your bad conduct was concerned?"

"No," came the reply.

The yob had been schooled in how to answer questions, and had a tight defence leaving virtually no opening for me to cross-examine.

"The defendant will say that you were ill-mannered and aggressive."

"Denied," said the yob.

"Is the defendant lying or mistaken?"

121

"Lying," came the reply.

"Thank you," I thought to myself, leaving me the opening I was looking for.

"There are three independent witnesses as to your behaviour and I think you will find they will say the same thing."

"What?" countered the yob, stealing time to gather his thoughts.

"They say your behaviour was loutish and aggressive, so do they lie as well?"

"They are friends - they are bound to support him."

I gritted my teeth,

"Are they lying? Forget whose friends they are."

"Yes, they are lying."

"Would it make any difference to your answer if I were to tell you that they are not his friends at all?" I continued.

"No," came the reply, "They look after their own in that pub."

"Were you rude to a lady in the bar?"

"There were no ladies in that bar."

"Alright, were you rude to a woman in the bar?"

"No."

"You told a woman in the bar to shift from the pool table."

"I asked her to move."

"You said shift. No please, no thank you, just shift."

"That's not an offence is it?"

"No of course not, but it's not very polite or gentlemanly is it?"

"So what?"

I was beginning to get behind his guard.

"You swore at the two lads playing pool because you thought they were taking their time?"

"They were."

"You accept that do you?"

"Yes."

I then referred to his statement to the police.

"You don't mention swearing in your statement?"

"I must have forgot, but that doesn't give him the right to attack me."

"Quite so, there's no excuse for grabbing someone by the throat either is there?"

"It depends."

"Well, lets look at what we agree between us. Did you grab anyone?"

"No."

"There are those who say you did just that."

"Inevitable - I was defending myself, they attacked me."

"The landlady will say that she served you with pints of lager on at least eight occasions."

"So...I like lager. I'm used to it, it doesn't make me drunk if that's what you're thinking."

"You drink it regularly do you, so you're used to it?"

"Yes."

"How many times a week?"

"Five."

"That's forty pints per week."

"Yes."

"That's a lot of money each week."

The yob did not reply.

"Well?" I asked, ramming down the point.

"I have lots of friends."

"Really, and I suppose they buy you the forty pints per week."

"Yes."

"The witnesses who I referred you to earlier all speak of you being drunk - what do you say about that?"

"I was not drunk."

"Not only were you drunk but you were aggressive and spoiling for a fight."

"How do you know, you weren't there."

"Fortunately, I was not there, but the witnesses have told me all about it. They're not lying - you are."

There was no answer, so I continued.

"Do you remember slamming money on the pool table?"

"No."

"Well I'm afraid to tell you that the witnesses have lied again - they say you did."

"It might have looked that way."

"How?"

"I put the money down, It may have sounded like slamming, and anyway that's how you register for a game."

"Do you do it when a player is taking a shot."

"You do it whenever you want."

"Oh, I see, you've never heard of manners then or common courtesy?"

Just then Neil interrupted and accused me of bullying the witness. I couldn't help thinking I had caught a nerve. So I continued.

"Did you grab my client's throat?"

"No."

"Can you explain to me how he had red marks around his neck?"

"No."

"It couldn't have been when you grabbed him then?"

"If I did grab him it was in self defence."

"How can you say that if you don't remember grabbing him at all?"

"I've just said it - and how did I get my injuries - who knocked me out, the man in the moon?"

The chairman interrupted. "Just answer the questions please," he said firmly.

"Can you remember anything of the incident outside?" I continued.

"Just being hit and that's it."

"So it may have been either of the young men who hit you?"

"Yes."

I realised I had an opening so I pursued it for all that I was worth.

"Would you be able to argue if I said, for example, it was the younger and smaller of the two men, the one with the hearing aid?"

"I couldn't argue with you but I know I was hit."

"Alright, I'll accept that for a moment, but if your memory was affected by the blow to the head and two days unconsciousness…

"Three days," interjected the youth.

"Three days, I corrected. "But you wouldn't be able to say who hit you or how it happened, would you?"

"I was hit."

"Yes, I know but if your memory has gone, you can't say how it happened?"

"Would you, being unconscious for three days?"

"No, I dare say I wouldn't have a clue how it happened or who did it."

"Exactly," said the youth.

"Exactly," I replied and promptly sat down - my point had been made. He couldn't say who hit him or in what circumstances so how had the prosecution proved assault? The next witness would be crucial. She was the lady at the bus stop.

As the yob left the witness box he stared at me aggressively. I looked the other way, but couldn't conceal a smile.

When the lady took the oath, she gave me the distinct impression that she did not want to be there. She was about eight and a half months pregnant and looked a little hot under the collar.

The chairman asked her to sit down to give her evidence, promising that she wouldn't be long. He stared at me with a look that said, "She won't be long will she?"

I took the point and sat back as Neil took her through the evidence.

She explained how she saw three men come out of the pub and there was a fight.

Neil explored her evidence carefully.

"How many of them fought?" asked Neil.

"I'm not sure, I think all of them, two definitely, and another got involved."

"How did it end?"

"The youth with the crew cut ended up on the floor. He banged his head when he fell. I remember thinking at the time that it was a nasty bump. I didn't expect him to get up and he didn't."

Neil sat down and I got up to cross examine.

The lady had no axe to grind. She was just doing her best to be truthful.

I smiled at her and asked if she wouldn't mind answering a few questions. She was at ease.

"You said in your evidence that there was a fight."

"Yes."

"You very fairly said that you're not sure how many fought."

"Yes."

"Is that because you didn't see them all exchange blows?"

"Well, yes, I suppose so."

"Could it be that two men were fighting and one was trying to break the other two up?"

"Well, yes, I suppose that's possible."

"Do I take it that you don't argue with me because I am right, or because it was not really clear from where you were standing?"

"It wasn't clear. You see it happened so quickly. One minute he was on his feet, the next he was down."

"So it wasn't a long sustained attack then?"

"Oh no, it was over in a flash"

"Just enough for one blow and that was it?"

"Possibly, I wouldn't like to say how many blows were exchanged."

"But could there have been just one?"

"Yes," she said thoughtfully, "There was a lot of shouting and the next minute the young man was on the floor."

"Shouting?" I asked.

"Yes, when they first came out the youth with the crew cut was shouting."

"How did he get outside?" I took a risk here because the yob had said that he was dragged out, and I might just jog her memory. It might not go in my favour.

"They walked."

"They walked."

"Yes, the short haired youth was shouting and there was a fight."

"Did you see the first blow?"

"I suppose so, but it was very confusing as it happened so quickly."

"But would you agree with me it was a short haired youth?"

"I couldn't disagree, and there was one blow, but again I'm not sure from whom."

"Could you disagree that the short haired youth was the aggressor?"

"Not really, he was certainly doing the shouting."

"He was angry."

"Sounded like it."

"Angry enough to hit out…" I waited for the interruption, but none came. Neil was as anxious for the truth as I was.

"I should say so," she replied.

Just as I was about to sit down, I took a deep breath and committed the sin to which good advocates should never succumb and that is to ask the proverbial one question too many.

"Which of the other two lads fought?" I had worked out my move. If she said Gary I would say self defence and if she said Richie, I would say Gary should not have been charged. If she wasn't sure, the prosecution hadn't proved their case.

"I think it was the smaller of the two."

The truth then hit me.

I knew why Gary did not want his brother to give evidence. I thanked the witness and sat down.

Neil wanted to re-examine and plug the holes I had created in his case but before he could do so the lady gave out a cry and asked for a drink.

"Are you alright?" he asked.

"My waters have broken," she exclaimed.

"So that's that Mr Franklin," I said, in the certain knowledge that the gaps in his case would remain completely unplugged.

A police officer was called and our witness was dispatched to the maternity wing of the local hospital without further delay. At 7.30pm the same day she was the proud mother of a bouncing baby girl who she named Verity, because she said that the truth very nearly came out in Rotherham court that day.

Once the courtroom had calmed down, I decided to submit to the court that the case should not proceed for the following reasons. Firstly, the yob's evidence did not explain how the incident had occurred. Secondly, he conceded that he did not know who had hit him, and thirdly, the independent witness described the skinhead as the aggressor and picked out Richie as the one responsible for the blow.

I knew the chairman was keen to leave and here was his ideal opportunity.

The magistrates retired and fifteen minutes later they sent for the clerk. This was not a good sign, because I expected that he would put the boot in and persuade the magistrates to refuse the submission. As it happened I was right. The submission was refused and the trial had to continue.

I called my client into the witness box.

Gary stood up to cross examination very well, and all three of my witnesses made it abundantly clear that the skinhead was not only drunk but aggressive. One of them told of seeing him drink three pints of snake bite, a lethal cocktail of cider and lager, a mixture the witness described as falling down material.

My lady witness was nothing less than magnificent. As she did not know Gary or Richie, she was obviously independent and she described how the skinhead had used bad language towards her. She said that she found his behaviour and attitude frightening and she went on to say that Gary interceded on her behalf, asking the skinhead to leave her alone. She described Gary as a little gentleman, and ended her evidence by saying the skinhead had grabbed Gary by the throat and pushed him outside, only releasing his grip in the doorway.

When Neil cross examined her, she gave a good account of herself. I felt that we were in the home straight. A good summing up speech from me and we had cracked it.

I waxed lyrically about the yob culture and reminded the bench of how Gary had tried to keep the peace. If he was

129

guilty of anything it was remonstrating with the skinhead for his bad manners and threatening behaviour towards a lady.

"How would you feel if your wife had been spoken to in that way?" I asked.

The bench nodded in approval, but I saved my best point until last.

"If the skinhead, for reasons best known to himself, can't remember what happened, and if the other prosecution witness agrees that it was the skinhead's fault, how can you convict the defendant of assault? And if, even if, which I doubt, you feel he has been assaulted, may I ask you by whom?"

I left it at that, the die was cast. There was no need to say anything else. We had walked it as far as I was concerned and even the police officer confirmed that Gary had maintained his story from start to finish.

"They will not be long," I thought to myself, and began to read the sports page in the paper, which Neil had pinched from the solicitor's room.

"What do you think Steve?" asked Gary.

"If I was a gambling man Gary, I would say it's a one horse race; but I don't gamble and I've done the job long enough not to make predictions." Our conversation was interrupted by a buzzer on the clerk's desk.

The clerk disappeared and with him went my confidence.

He returned and announced that the bench had a question to ask and he thought it would be best asked in open court.

The chairman read from a piece of paper.

"How did the complainant get to the public house?"

I looked at Neil, and he returned my look of amazement. We were both perplexed by the question.

"What has that got to do with it?" asked Neil.

"God knows," I whispered. The clerk confidentially announced that there was no evidence on that point. The chairman asked if any could be called, but Neil ventured that we had both finished our cases and as such the evidence was closed. With that the bench retired again.

"What the bloody hell is that about?" I asked. I must admit I was beginning to twitch a little as the adrenaline glands worked overtime.

"Don't worry," said Neil, "You're home and dry. No one will count on that evidence."

I welcomed the assurance as Neil and I looked at the paper together.

"Look at this," said Neil as he read out the headline. "Defence solicitor censured for disrespect to the bench," he laughed. There was no such headline.

"Oh, look at this," I said, reading aloud in reply.

"Prosecution solicitor kicked up the arse for being a twat."

Neil smiled and made his customary gesture.

Thirty minutes later I asked the clerk what the problem was.

"As you well know Mr Smith, I do not make the decisions and I am not privy to what the magistrates discuss."

"You belong in a privy," I replied, sarcastically.

"I beg your pardon?" asked the clerk.

"What is there to decide? It's the most straight forward case for an acquittal I have ever had."

"It's not for me to say," said the clerk with an air of self righteousness.

"Oh, come on - it's never proved in a million years."

"You shouldn't get so involved," said the clerk.

I turned to Neil and mouthed the word 'shithead.' Neil smiled and continued to read his paper.

My thoughts were interrupted by Gary.

"What ever they say Steve, thanks for everything and thanks for keeping Richie out of it."

I just nodded and went to use the phone. The office told me that my 3.30pm client had left in a huff and my 4.00pm was asleep in a drunken stupor. Jarvis had rung and cancelled our dinner and the gents' toilet was blocked. The VAT man had telephoned the cashier and been his customary rude self and I was thinking of ways to upset him when the buzzer went and the bench walked in. They looked away from Gary, which sent a shiver down my spine as it was a bad omen,

"We find the case proved, you're guilty of assault.........."

I did not catch the end of what the chairman said. I looked at the bench in complete bewilderment as if to say, "Why?" or "You're joking."

"Have you anything to add Mr Franklin?" said the chairman.

"No sir, except I'll hand in the defendant's record."

The skinhead thrust his fist into the air and shouted "Yes," from the back of the court. The chairman then spoke to me, "Do you wish to say anything Mr Smith?"

I must confess that I had to summon up every ounce of discipline from my soul, not to embarrass myself with unsuitable expletives. In the event I just shook my head and bit my lip. I was so angry that I drew blood. I looked at Franklin. He simply lifted his eyebrows and looked away. I glanced to the back of the courtroom and noticed Richie. He had realised that his brother had been found guilty. The look on his face said it all. Gary was innocent, but Richie.....well that's another story.

The chairman announced,

"In view of your criminal record we feel that a prison sentence is appropriate. Have you anything to add Mr Smith?"

I replied quickly,

"Will the court order a probation report to look into the defendant's background?"

"We do not have to order a report if we think prison in inevitable," said the chairman.

"Yes," I said, "But common sense dictates a report should be ordered in this case.   I submit you can't sentence properly without one."

The magistrates exchanged their views in whispers and proceeded without retiring.

"Stand up," said the chairman to Gary.   "We think this is a serious offence of violence in a public house."

"No it wasn't," I said to myself, "It was not that serious and it took place outside in the street."

The chairman continued,

"You have previous convictions, and the one we note was for violence only three months ago.   Accordingly, we feel imprisonment is warranted.   You will therefore go to prison for six months."

I threw my pen down in disgust.   Gary raised a smile which he directed to me on his way to the cell.   He waved to Richie before disappearing down the spiral staircase leading to the cells.

"I'm surprised by that," whispered Neil.   "You'll appeal, of course?"

"Just you watch me," I replied and quickly stood to address the bench once again.

"I would respectfully ask the court to consider bail pending appeal.   The defendant has been on bail throughout without breach."

"Had you better take instructions first?" said the chairman.

"No thank you, Sir," I replied, "I can assure you he will want an appeal."

After a short whispered deliberation, the chairman spoke again.

"Bail is refused, the court will rise."

Before I got the chance to spoil my manners and damage my career irreparably, the bench retired. After they had gone, I began a tirade of abuse that left both myself and Neil breathless.

As the court emptied, I was left alone except for the solitary figure of a young man standing at the back of the court. He was extremely confused as I knew he could sense my anger.

Richie spoke just one word in the form of a question.

"Prison?"

"Yes," I replied, nodding. I held up six fingers.

"No!" said Richie.

"Yes, but he will serve...." And this time I kept three fingers raised.

"Wrong," said Richie.

"Yes, I know," I replied.

I directed Richie to the cells by the public entrance and made my way down the spiral staircase.

"That was a bit over the top," said the court sergeant as I passed him.

I was too angry to reply and then Gary was brought out of the cell to see me. His accommodation was more suitable for a black museum rather than a place to keep human beings in the 1980's. Times had changed, but not the Rotherham cells and I realised that a proper cell in a prison might be a welcome relief.

"Thanks for everything," said Gary, reassuring me.

"But you got the maximum," I replied, "You could not get any more. They did not even ask for a probation report."

"No, but it's over now. I would not do community service or probation anyway, and I will be out in three months."

I was quite surprised by Gary's acceptance of his fate.

"I have told them we are to appeal, I will apply for bail to a judge in chambers pending appeal. At the very least it will bring the appeal hearing forward."

Gary thought for a moment and then spoke.

"I don't want to appeal. If I do, everything gets looked at again, doesn't it?"

"Yes," I replied, dismissing his foolishness, "But that's what we want."

"No," said Gary firmly. "That's not what I want. We had a go and we lost, it's best forgotten now."

I had spent the majority of my life talking people out of appealing and justifying prison sentences, so this was a novel change. Despite everything I had to say, including the fact that he had nothing to lose, Gary was intransigent. "I don't suppose you would like to explain why?" I asked.

"It's over now," Gary replied, "Would you tell Richie I'm OK and I'll sent him a Visiting Order as soon as I can. Thanks again." With that, Gary returned to his cell. I looked through the spy hole in the door and observed Gary looking into space, waiting for the realisation of what had happened to hit him.

"Can't his brother see him sergeant?" I asked the reluctant jailer.

"Of course, but only for five minutes. The prison bus is on its way."

"OK, I'll tell him," I replied.

I left via the large green door, damaged with years of graffiti and the names of some distinguished defendants who had enjoyed the hospitality, etched in crude form. As the door had been painted fresh names had been scratched over older ones. One name in particular caught my attention.

"Albert was 'ere once." The word 'once' had a line through it and had been replaced with 'twice' which in turn had been crossed out and replaced with 'three times'.

I smiled to myself before spotting Richie, who was sitting on the wall outside the court.. As I looked at him, I realised I had fallen foul of one of the biggest mistakes you can make in this job; taking the results personally. You simply shouldn't get involved and must remember always that tomorrow is another day. However, as I looked at Richie sitting there alone, friendless and confused, I couldn't help thinking that they could stuff the job. How I hate dealing with cases when the courts get it wrong. Fortunately for me, it did not happen very often, but when it did.............

My thoughts were interrupted by Richie's strained voice.

"It's wrong," said Richie, whose limited powers of communication from his silent world exasperated him.

"Not him, not him," was all he continued to say.

"Yes, I know," I replied, nodding firmly. "I realise that," I said mouthing each word correctly.

The door then opened again and the sergeant signalled to Richie to come and see his brother before he left to start his prison sentence.

As Richie was walking away I said,

"It was you, wasn't it?" but Richie had his back to me and he didn't catch what I said.

The door slammed firmly shut on him and the case itself. It was 5.30pm and I was playing football at 6.00pm. '

Chapter Eight

ALBERT'S PIGEON

Allotments are as much a part of northern life as pints of beer, Woodbines and bread and dripping sandwiches. Over the years almost every species of plant has been cultivated and many types of animals have been reared on the allotments of the north of England. Apart from providing produce for the dinner tables of the allotment holders, the open spaces gave working men somewhere to develop hobbies and interests. Looking over any area of allotments, you will see monuments of all shapes, sizes and colours built in honour of the noble racing pigeon.

Pigeon racing has a large and fanatical following with many participants spending more time and money on their pigeons than on their families. To rear a champion racing pigeon was a dream of many of the allotment holders in Rotherham where Jack and Albert shared two adjoining allotments, one of which was Jack's by right and the other was Albert's due to the fact that it had been his grandad's until he had died. Jack had merely 'forgotten' to inform the council of the fact that the allotment should be re-allocated to the person on the top of the waiting list.

Jack's talents were growing vegetables, racing pigeons, and thieving. His vegetables always grew, his pigeons always won but Jack was always caught. For Jack, two out of three was pretty good and there was always the chance that he would get away with it next time.

His son Albert had been brought up with allotment life and the daily trips to the 'garden' were a regular feature of the family's routine. Here, Jack spent much of the time teaching his son two of his three talents. Thieving seemed to be in the

Heptonstall genes and as such did not need to be taught. If Jack was the worst thief in Rotherham he was also the best racing pigeon breeder by far.

On their allotment, there were two sheds. The first was quite dilapidated but the other, which housed his prized pigeons, had been constructed with loving care and, in Jack's words, was "fit to live in". Indeed it was, if you were a pigeon. It was clear that no expense had been spared in ensuring the comfort of the inhabitants. The whole place was water tight and draught free, and any self respecting pigeon would be proud to perch beneath its portals.

Jack's pride and joy was a racing pigeon which he had named 'Arse'. It was a peculiar name for a pigeon, and indeed it was a peculiar name for anything except an arse, but that was it's name and Jack's Arse was the talk of the pigeon mad neighbourhood.

He had won five races on the trot, or rather on the wing, the last one being one of the "Grand Nationals" of the local racing world, the Ingoldmells classic. For this, Jack won a prestigious trophy, £500.00 in cash and a fortnight's holiday in a caravan at Ingoldmells, a popular seaside resort on the Lincolnshire coast. It was said that the second prize was three weeks in the same caravan.

Some of Jack's winnings went on beer, some on the purchase of a black and white portable television set for the allotment, and the rest was invested in a flock of geese which Jack later told me were better than a pair or rottweilers for guarding the allotment.

Arse became the attention of many breeders in the pigeon world and Jack received a number of substantial offers to put Arse into stud. He turned them all down prior to the 'big one', which was the race to be held at Fleetwood. The winner would receive a handsome prize but, more importantly, the winning pigeon's value would increase substantially.

Jack had offered to take me on a guided tour of his pigeon lofts many times but I had always found suitable excuses. However, when Jack showed me a photograph of the trophies which Arse had won, I decided to take a look at this wonder bird when I was next in the area.

Arse's fame had spread throughout the area and during the evenings when Jack was away from the allotment he would leave Albert or one of his brothers on guard. As there were so many children to choose from they were able to work a shift system which meant that Arse could be looked after around the clock. I arrived late one Wednesday afternoon to be greeted by Jack and three of his sons, the ubiquitous Albert, together with 'our Morris' and 'our Venn'.

The three brothers were standing in a line like ornamental toby jugs, all with the same posture, but more particularly with the same wide grin dominating each face. I was in no doubt they were Jack's sons and the local milkman had certainly played no part in their conception.

It was my first introduction to 'our Venn'. He was an older version of Albert, with the same straw like hair and preponderance of gums.

"That's a strange name?" I asked.

"Argh," said Jack, "It should have been 'Ken' but I 'ad flu when I registered him and the Registrar didn't 'ear me properly. We never noticed it until we got to the church for the christening, so we just left it at that."

I had always been fascinated by the strong family bond which existed between Jack and his brood. While they were all villains, they had an endearing quality unlike most of the local 'Mafia'. The suggestion that there is honour among thieves is more often found in fiction than in fact, but it was fairly near the mark as far as this family was concerned.

Jack and Madge loved their children and they were cared for to the best of their financial ability and on occasions, someone else's financial ability but, for all that they were villains, they had their own moral code. They would never burgle a dwellinghouse, rob an old lady or pillage the purse of the man in the street. Commercial premises, however, were fair game, believing as they did that insurance companies were rich pickings for this latter day Robin Hood's band.

All their children were very respectful, both to their parents and adults in general, but it was best not to cross them, because if you 'had to feight one you had to feight them all'. As a result their only 'predators' were the police and security men everywhere.

I surveyed the area of both allotments to find them particularly neat and tidy. Good husbandry was obvious and the sight of row after row of vegetables in regimented order left me in no doubt as to the family's abilities.

I saw every vegetable imaginable, from cauliflower to asparagus, shallots to runner beans. On the second allotment there were well constructed sheds for hens and a fenced area which housed the geese, who were not only messy and noisy but extremely aggressive, taking the greatest exception to my presence.

One of them tried to get me through the wicker work fence, but Albert came to my rescue and, with a few words and a flick of his fingers to the back of my attacker's head, the beast was subdued almost as if by magic.

"E's gorra way wi' them birds," said Jack, "E can make em do owt. Watch this."

He turned to Albert, who made some gesticulation which was clearly an invitation for the geese to perform their party tricks.

To Jack's great delight, the flock made noise to order and then went quiet again with a wave of Albert's hand, then they hopped about madly as if dancing for an enthralled audience.

When the performance had finished the family clapped their hands vigorously and I found myself joining in, almost as if we had witnessed some spectacular circus act. Albert then proudly presented me with two large eggs and I was advised to eat them as soon as possible, before they 'went off'.

The conducted tour lasted some twenty minutes, pausing at each section to give me samples of the produce. I filled my car boot with all manner of home grown veg before being taken on the highlight of the tour; the pigeon loft.

There were about thirty pigeons in all, housed in a number of separate apartments. The loft was warm and quite cosy, but there, at the top, on its own, was a part of the shed more salubrious than the rest. Jack stood back and with a beaming smile he proudly introduced me to his favourite, and with great pride he announced,

"This......is my Arse."

I paused for a moment before speaking, not knowing whether to laugh or cry. Jack broke the silence.

"Ee's fastest bird this side o' Pennines tha knows, I'd back 'im against owt. Mindst thee, 'ees well looked after, ee wants for nowt, good seed, good pellets, rainwater and a bit of 'that there'."

"A bit of 'that there'? I queried

"Ahh, Uncle Jack's magic energy pills.

"Energy pills?" I queried further.

"Ahh, it's a like a supplement tha knows...........:.....it gis 'im some oumph."

"My God," I thought to myself, "Jack's drugging the bloody bird." I had heard of such things in dog and horse racing, but not pigeons.

141

"Jack," I said firmly, "You know it's illegal to use drugs, don't you?"

"I don't do drugs Mr Smith," said Jack, "Not even for me, for me family and certainly not for me pigeons."

"No, I'm sorry Jack, I didn't want to give that impression, but I was just intrigued as to what energy pills you were referring to?"

"I've got me own formula," said Jack in a most self satisfied manner.

"I mix up some glucose, some yeast and some stuff I get from 'erbert Micklethwaite."

"Who's 'erbert Micklethwaite?" I asked

"He races dogs and he's given 'em energy pills as well."

"Oh," I said curiously, "What is in the powder from 'erbert Micklethwaite?"

"Dun't know," said Jack, "But it certainly makes em shift. Cage gets a bit full, but they'll shift alright."

"What do you mean the cage gets a bit full?" I asked.

"Tha knows, with shit."

"Oh," I said, "I understand what you mean. I suppose it facilitates a positive reaction in the digestive tract," I said, believing I had put the matter extremely well.

"No, it just makes 'em shit," said Jack.

I thought that I would leave the subject of the pigeon's bowels and proceed to familiarise myself, albeit on a superficial level, with the do's and don'ts of pigeon racing.

Showing my ignorance of the subject, I set about asking what many well informed pigeon racers would realise was a ludicrous question.

"It's amazing how they know where to fly back to" I ventured.

Jack looked at his boys, and they at him. The Heptonstall grin hit me from all sides and for once they had the advantage, and perhaps on this occasion the arse that I was talking out of was my own.

Doing his best to hide the smile, Albert announced,

"They are 'oming pigeons Mr Smith."

The position was as clear as mud and, being none the wiser, I decided to leave it at that.

"Cast your eyes on this Mr Smith," said Jack, and he presented a small container connected to a car battery. He took from it a small polystyrene box and there, encased in cotton wool, was a small blue egg.

"See that," said Jack, "That's worth a grand of anybody's money."

I was perplexed, so I asked him what it was.

"That, my old cock," said Jack, "Is Arse II."

"Ah, son of Arse," I ventured.

"Ah," said Jack. "It's in incubation. I've already 'ad offers for that egg."

It surprised me that a pigeon's egg could have such a high value, but such is the pigeon world.

Jack carefully placed the egg back into its container, then into the box and then re-connected the various wires which lay around his bench.

When I left the shed I noticed a rather unique locking and security device.

"You're keen on security, then, Jack?" I volunteered.

"Certainly am Mr Smith. You can't trust anybody around 'ere, they would 'ave the fillings art thee teeth."

The disdain with which Jack spoke of the criminal classes fascinated me, for he clearly did not include himself as a member. I left the loft and walked back down the gravel path which led to my car. Three toby jugs lined up to wave me off and with a click of his fingers Albert made the geese, who were incarcerated nearby, flap their wings, in tribute to my visit.

I congratulated Jack on his fine 'spread' and said that all he needed was running water and a toilet to make the place perfect.

"Argh, we mek do with a bucket in t' shed," said Jack.

I found myself waving to all of them as I got into the car, but not before noticing that my windscreen had been in the flight path of late arrivals to the pigeon loft. I put on the windscreen wipers only to find that the washers were empty. Seeing my plight, Albert came out of the shed with a bucket and threw its contents across my windscreen. I started the windscreen wipers as the 'water' cascaded down the glass and onto the bonnet. It cleared the screen, although it smelt stronger than water.

When I returned to the office, via the local car wash, I was in a very good mood. All appeared to be going well, although I was putting in a lot of hours and I had started to work on Saturday mornings, but even that was enjoyable as I knew it was benefiting the business. What awaited me was to change my mood quite considerably.

We had been carrying out a great deal of work for a local haulage firm which had about sixty employees. The firm had approximately one million pounds worth of assets and, while they never paid their bills on time, they paid...eventually.

They had run up a considerable bill with us to the tune of some two thousand pounds, a substantial sum in 1983, especially for a small firm like ours.

The day before, Wilf had been trying to chase them, but unfortunately there had been no answer. That morning, when the post arrived, we were to find out why. The company had gone into liquidation and the assets in no way cleared the substantial deficits. There was talk of ten pence in the pound, but when Wilf spoke to the official receiver he couldn't even promise that.

Our otherwise idyllic business life had taken a tremendous blow. For the first time since we set up in business together we had to face one of the cruel realities of life.

It had always been our practice when incurring bills on behalf of clients to 'have the money up front', but as this firm was one of our major clients, we had not asked for sufficient funds to pay their disbursements, the bills we had incurred on their behalf during the case, but had invoiced them for the full amount on completion of the case.

As our name was on a number of invoices which totalled over £500.00, the outcome was that we had done about one years work for the firm and would have to pay five hundred pounds of our own money for the privilege.

The directors had fled and all we could get from the official receivers was a dose of sympathy.

I went to the Rotherham Magistrates' Court that morning with a heavy heart and, for the first time, a substantial business worry around my neck. At that time we had only the smallest of overdrafts, but this deficit would mean a trip to see our bank manager. Formerly, he had always come to visit us, but I discovered that a bank manager's attitude changes somewhat when you are in the 'red'. It is then that you find he is not really the bank manager at all, but simply the messenger of his head office, something you never hear about until you are in debt.

For the first time since we opened the office I failed to get a full night's sleep. The atmosphere at work had changed. The buoyancy, good spirit and joviality appeared to have gone. All manner of things along the line were affected. The holiday which I had planned for later that year had to go, as did the new car and the painting scheme for the office. The spring in my step had disappeared.

The staff were the first to notice because we had no experience of putting on a brave face. The old maxim of 'you live and learn' was never more true than at that time. It was then I realised that the word 'if' is the most obnoxious word in the English language.

"If only we had done this" and "if only we had done that," were comments which we both made but, after a week of brooding, I was determined to try to put it to one side and vowed never to let it happen again.

My love affair with self-employment had suffered its first blow and things were never to be quite the same again. Unfortunately, that numbing feeling in the stomach when bad news arrives was to visit me again. By the end of the week I had come to terms with what had happened and had fixed an appointment for us to visit the bank manager with a view to extending our overdraft. At lunchtime we were to treat him to a four course meal at Reilleys Restaurant at Crosspool, Sheffield.

For once I was on time and Wilf and I drove to the restaurant where our guest was waiting. We thought that the offer of a free lunch might endear us to him and to some extent break down the barrier that would exist between two people cap in hand seeking money and another who was in the position to provide it. The lunch went well, as did the meeting, and our credit was good enough to be awarded an overdraft facility of £20,000.00. It was a huge amount by our standards and was yet another commitment to be paid out of an already shrinking cake.

As we were drinking glasses of port, the bank manager's was a double, we were interrupted by a member of the restaurant staff saying that there was an urgent telephone call for me in reception.

I excused myself and took the call. It was the custody sergeant at Rotherham police station, who laughed when he apologised for interrupting my lunch.

"A Mr Jack Heptonstall and his son, who refuses to give his name, are requesting your attendance at the police station. The allegation is one of theft."

He paused as he flicked through the papers, then I heard him laugh again.

"Is there something funny?" I queried, being none too pleased at having my lunch interrupted.

"I think so," said the sergeant. "You see, it's the nature of the charge and what they have actually stolen, but I'll tell you when you get to the station. Are you coming or what?"

"It's got to be 'what', as I'm not finished."

"Oh, I'm frightfully sorry," said the Sargeant, "I hope that we are not downing too many brandies. We wouldn't want you to be driving over the limit, Mr Smith now would we?"

"No, we wouldn't," I said to him sarcastically. "Besides, I don't drink brandy."

"I would have enjoyed a brandy myself today," said the sergeant, nonchalantly, "But I'm having to work here in this cesspit, doing my best for society and the public at large."

"Well done Sergeant," I said. "How important it is that we have people like you bothering people like me." With that I announced I would be along within an hour and returned to our guest.

I had agreed to drive that day and consequently had limited my drinking to just the one glass of port. Wilf and the bank manager however had made merry throughout the meal with copious quantities of alcohol.

147

Eventually, I managed to force them into my car and dropped them off at the Cross Keys in Rotherham so they could have a 'last one' leaving me to travel to the police station.

When I got to the charge office there was much hilarity. In a little room was a gentleman in a most harassed and aggressive state. He was making a statement which contained a liberal dose of expletives.

Another man was being violently sick near the breathalyser machine and a third was screaming down the telephone to his wife, demanding that she bring some cigarettes and a clean pair of underpants. Sitting in the middle of the chaos was Sergeant David Brown, who had just taken over the charge office duties from the officer who had rung me. I had known Sergeant Brown for sometime, since his days when he was in the CID. He had invested twenty-five years of his life in the police service and had seen it all, or most of it. He surveyed the scene in the room, shrugged his shoulders and shook his head.

He had the air about him of a man who was close to retirement.

"Excuse me one moment Mr Smith, if you would please," he said to me politely.

"Certainly Sergeant," I replied, and stood back while he went about sorting out the whole mess before him. He turned first to the man on the telephone.

"Would you limit your call to the next ten seconds please and return to your cell."

The man protested, but Sergeant Brown continued,

"I said ten seconds which is now eight seconds, whereupon the phone will be taken away and you will be taken back to a cell. Conclude it now, no ifs, no buts, no pack drill. Simply do as I say. This is my charge office, my phone, my time and my cell, but it's going to be your cell, so put that phone down and take a casual walk to it.

He then turned his attention to the man who was still vomiting.

"PC Withers," speaking firmly to his special constable assistant. "Find a shovel and a mop and give it to our guest and tell him to clean it up."

He then turned his attention to the interview room and shouted,

"Hey, you in there, stop bloody shouting and fucking swearing, I'm trying to conduct a fucking charge office procedure. If you must fucking swear keep it bloody quiet and at least shut the fucking door." He then turned to me, smiled and spoke most politely.

"Good afternoon Mr Smith, how nice to see you again. How can we help you?"

I couldn't help smiling, but I played along and asked if I could see Jack and Albert Heptonstall.

"Of course you can. I have a copy of the custody record which will give you all the details you require."

He then took the custody record, looked at it, and smiled. Before he could say anything, his assistant had brought Jack and Albert out of their cell.

They both smiled when they saw me and I detected a hint of relief on their faces. Jack was the first to speak:

"They have got me this time Mr Smith. Bang to rights, I've had to admit it."

I was surprised at the sudden burst of honesty, but on the basis that he was 'bang to rights' it seemed there was little else that could be done. Even Albert had supplied his name and address, so the game was clearly up.

The officers appeared and were ready to carry out the interview, and on the basis that there was no argument about guilt and the fact that both Jack and Albert were anxious to return to their allotment, I agreed to start it straight away.

As we walked down the corridor to the interview room with the police officers, Jack spoke:

"We've got to get off as soon as we can because no one is looking after our Arse and the egg."

The officers looked perplexed, and one of them spoke.

"I've heard of 'watch your back', but I have never heard of 'watch your arse'," he said smiling. I didn't reply and we went into the interview room.

I allowed Jack and Albert to sit down as I spoke to the officers outside to establish just what was going on. They couldn't conceal their laughter.

"Just what is going on?" I said, "Every time I try to talk about this case everyone bursts out laughing."

"Well," said DC Sutton, "I think I can explain why. You see, Jack and Albert have stolen a transportable lavatory which contains a chemical toilet. It is housed in a small trailer which is carried on two wheels and attaches to a vehicle with a tow bar in the same way as a caravan, but obviously with a different purpose. At 8.30 this morning, witnesses will say that the said item was parked outside the workings at the council offices for use by the workmen who are engaged on that site. At approximately 10.00am the said item was seen to be leaving the site being pulled by a transit van driven by the defendant Jack. Albert was in the passenger seat. The said item was then transported to an allotment on the outskirts of town, that said allotment being owned by the said Jack. Unfortunately for your client, he was seen removing the said item from the site and within twenty minutes of the theft police officers arrived at the allotment where the said item was found."

150

I interrupted and asked whether they could prove that it was the same chemical toilet.

The officer interrupted me in return, grinned, and said,

"We have an eye witness Mr Smith, not only as to the theft, but to the journey and also the delivery of the said item to the allotment site."

I queried this suggestion.

"How could you do that, did you follow him?" I asked.

"No," said the officer biting his lip to try to stop himself laughing. "But unfortunately for your clients, and indeed unfortunately for the poor witness involved, someone was actually using the said lavatory at the time of the theft and was still present in the said trailer when it arrived at the allotment. The person concerned is the rather irate gentleman giving a statement to one of my colleagues in the little room off the charge office.

It seems that he was actually in the act of toiletry, as it were, when he describes that the toilet 'jerked', whereupon he was thrown off the seat and onto the floor where, owing to the speed with which the vehicle was travelling, he found himself rolling about on the floor causing him great discomfort, slight grazing to his buttocks and heavy soiling of his clothing.

The officer had done an extremely good job of describing the facts with as straight a face as possible, but unfortunately the humour of the situation got the better of him and he burst into laughter at the same time as I did. It was a matter of a minute or so before we regained our composure, entered the room and spoke to my clients.

"Did you know that there was someone using the toilet when you pinched it?" I asked looking from Jack to Albert and back from Albert to Jack.

There was no answer, but suddenly the huge grin that usually covered my clients' faces re-appeared. They looked at each other and before they could answer they both burst into uncontrollable fits of laughter. Again I had to compose myself, but it was some minutes before I could get Jack and Albert in a fit state to be interviewed.

The matter was all the more embarrassing because Rotherham had just started a pilot scheme for interviews to be recorded on a tape machine. Eventually, all parties were positioned in the small interview room.

The interview went well until the police referred to the unfortunate witness who was found in a state of undress when the police arrived. In a rather tense situation like that, the slightest thing can bring about mass hilarity.

As soon as the officer mentioned the man in the toilet, Jack burst into laughter. There is something infectious about laughter and on that day it infected me. I too had to laugh. Unfortunately, the situation got the better of the police as well and they joined in with the result that a complete farce was recorded. Laughter was followed by coughing which was followed by a short silence as everyone composed themselves. However, a further question would trigger the laughing fits again.

Eventually the interview was completed and Jack admitted his guilt, as did Albert. The police couldn't destroy the tapes because they were actually pieces of evidence in the case but fortunately, they never had to be played, except by me whenever depression rears its ugly head.

Eventually, Jack and Albert were released and I waited for them in the foyer of the police station while their photographs and fingerprints were taken for the umpteenth time.

When they re-appeared they were still laughing.

"Why on earth did you steal a chemical toilet?" I asked.

"Do you remember when you came to see our allotments?" said Albert.

"You said then that the only thing we needed was a toilet and we 'ad cracked it."

"Yes, but I didn't mean you should go out and steal one, and besides it's got 'Rotherham Borough Council' printed all over it."

"Ah well," said Jack, "We were going to paint that over. We would 'ave just blanked it out and tha couldn't 'ave read it."

I was in despair as there was little point in discussing it further.

As we got outside the police station, Jack asked me for a lift, as he had no money for bus fares.

As I dropped Jack and Albert off at the allotment I noticed that the toilet had already been towed away by the police, but there was a considerable amount of activity around the pigeon loft. I waited to see what was happening, only to be waved in by Jack, who shouted,

"Mr Smith, come and see! Come and see!!"

I was a little dubious because I thought that it might be something which I wouldn't want to see, but I was assured it was safe, and when I went inside I saw a number of Jack's family surrounding the bench beneath Arse's cage. The room was silent, and as I peered down into the incubation box I saw the signs of a crack through the centre of the egg. In the minutes that followed I was privy to the birth of Arse Junior. 'Oos' and 'Ahhhs' surrounded the little object, who was quite the most ugly thing I had ever seen. I looked into Jack's face and noticed his eyes sparkling. He looked at the little object and announced,

"Isn't 'e beautiful?"

I looked, but couldn't possibly agree. I looked back at Jack, but all I could see in his face were pound signs. I had not realised that I had been privy to the birth of a legend.

It was too private a moment to stay and so I went to my car and set off back to the office, but not before I fought my way past six broody geese.

As I drove into the car park, I saw a familiar face leave the bank across the road, having great difficulty in walking towards the railway station. It seemed that everyone had had a good day.

Chapter Nine

GUNFIGHT AT THE OK WORKING MEN'S CLUB

It was the summer of 1983. Council workers were busy watering the town's display of hanging baskets and flowering shrubs. The mornings were greeted with a gentle mist which disappeared by lunchtime exposing the fierce glare of the sun in a cloudless sky. At lunchtimes, jacketless men in short-sleeved shirts wandered around the town centre and the local park with their sandwiches and cans of pop, viewing the local girls resplendent in skimpy sportswear.

By night-time the cocktail of heat and alcohol led to many a skirmish outside the public houses and nightclubs.

While those ingredients are present there will always be work available for people like me. Sometimes it comes from unexpected sources and on one occasion from South Kirkby, a small mining village near Pontefract. Its main features were a large pit and as many pubs as you could visit in a week. The local economy relied almost exclusively on the mines. If you did not work at the local pit, you were doing something connected with it or serving it and its people. It was home to a man called Bruce Johnson.

Bruce had been a miner from being seventeen years old He had a good job and, despite the appalling conditions in which he and his colleagues had to work, he enjoyed a reasonable income, particularly if he managed to work an extra shift. He was thirty-eight and apart from a 'miners' chest he was a fairly healthy specimen. He was a little over six feet tall with a shock of long curly blonde hair and, although he had a boxers nose, his facial features retained the winsome contours of youth which brought him considerable favour amongst the women in the locality. He was sixteen stone of pure muscle and as "fit as a butcher's dog". He kept fit by working out with weights and running at night with his dog 'Goz'.

The main problem with Bruce was his inability to turn away from a fight.

He was a confirmed bachelor but enjoyed many a discreet, and sometimes not so discreet liaison with a number of girlfriends who doted upon him. Taking all things into account, he had a reasonably happy lifestyle.

However, in mid August on a very warm evening an incident occurred in the South Kirby Working Mens' Club which resulted in Bruce Johnson being charged with assault occasioning actual bodily harm and breach of the peace.

The concert room was the focal point of the entertainment that night and, being the largest room in the building, it housed the majority of the clientele. The other reason for the large gathering was the 'cheap beer night' making the club a magnet for the drinkers in the community.

The entertainer or 'turn' as they are commonly referred to in Yorkshire was the aptly named Dwight Dazzle, known during the day at the bakery where he worked as Cyril Beevers. His hobby and part time job was to entertain in the local clubs with his rather high-pitched voice singing the songs made famous by the Irish tenor Joseph Locke.

Cyril was thirty-five and owing to premature baldness, had to wear a toupee. Unfortunately, it did not fit properly and it was the wrong colour. Cyril was wearing a black dinner jacket, with a ruffled fronted shirt with red and black zig zag lines down it. The bow tie was blue and beneath it was a large medallion which bore the initials SCT. On closer scrutiny, the words below the initials read 'Sheffield City Transport', but Cyril knew it looked good from a distance. Dwight was avuncular in appearance and, though not trained, had a pleasant voice, but his presentation suffered from him being short tongued. His transit van leaked and the seats were always wet, and this aggravated his persistent complaint of piles.

Success on the local club scene was measured by applause or indifference or, if the act failed, booing and abuse and, in isolated cases, even assault and battery. Dwight usually managed indifference from his audience, which was an achievement in this particular club. It was expected that the 'turn' would withstand four separate forays onto the stage for periods of about twenty minutes each. Introductions were usually made in the first two spots but thereafter there was little point as the audience grew in numbers, restlessness and volume.

The concert secretary, otherwise known as the 'referee', was there to introduce the acts and try to keep the audience quiet during the performances. He attempted to achieve this almost impossible task by switching the house lights on and off in the area of the noise and via rather unfortunate interruptions using the house microphone while the acts were in progress. Integral passages of songs where the singer was trying to achieve feelings of emotion would often be interrupted by cries of,

"Give order, please, let turn get it o'er with - thank you please".

This particular evening poor old Dwight was singing his heart out against a background of,

"Quiet please," and, "gi'ore, let the poor bugger sing," and the house lights generally being flashed on and off rather like those in a disco. It was not a fitting background for the old David Whitfield song, 'Cara Mia Mine', but Dwight had seen it all before and his skin was as thick as a woodbine packet.

"Cara mia mine won't you say goodbye," sang Dwight as a large pot bellied customer walked in front of the stage carrying two pint glasses for a re-fill with beer. He winked at the people sat on a table near the front of the stage and shouted, "All reight George."

He had to shout to make himself heard above the nuisance of the singer who had the audacity to interrupt his conversation by singing. Before the song had finished, the pot bellied man returned again, walking in front of the stage and Dwight before pausing at the table he had acknowledged on the first half of his trip.

"Ah you allreight Stanley?" came the reply.

"Well arghh George apart from't prostrate, it's giving me bollocks some 'ammer tha knows," said Stanley.

The audience seemed to pay more attention to Stanley's prostrate than Dwight's rendition of "Cara Mia", but then he was standing in the flight path of the spotlight which danced about Stanley's bald patch as though it was a target.

It's not stopped thee supping ale," shouted a large woman with a blue rinse sitting nearby, encouraged by the laughter of her friends.

As Stanley turned to speak to her, Dwight hit his last note with a resounding flourish. There was no applause apart from the concert secretary, who stopped when his pipe accidentally fell from his mouth, hit the microphone on its way to the desk and caused a loud ringing noise to emanate from the speaker system.

"Oh fuck," he announced as the pipe broke in two. Unfortunately the microphone, was still on and the concert secretary's words rang out just as Dwight was taking his bow. Dwight looked for the concert secretary, who by this time was under his desk and cursing like a "good un."

The audience began to get up: not to give Dwight a standing ovation but to queue for bingo tickets.

Later that evening Bruce walked from the concert room to the toilets and occupied a urinal next to Hedley Salter, the local yob. Hedley was in his late 30's, a large, balding man, with tobacco stained false teeth, a permanent sneer and an inclination towards violence. In short, he was the town bully and was universally disliked, and feared by many.

He had been involved in a beer drinking contest with a group of his acquaintances: he had no friends and the beer had loosened his tongue.

Looking over into Bruce's urinal, Hedley could not resist an ill timed, and ill conceived comment.

"Ar dunt reckon much to that," said Hedley contemptuously.

"What's tha mean?" asked Bruce.

"Tha'll not do much damage with that. There's no wonder tha can't keep a bird."

Bruce felt inclined to reply in kind.

"And what's tha call that then?" he said, staring at his counterpart's apparel. "I've seen more head on a pint of flat mild."

Unfortunately Hedley was in no mood for repartee and took the comment to heart.

"Thar's nowt but a fat twat," said Hedley aggressively.

"Nobody calls me fat," said Bruce and almost simultaneously they grabbed each other and a brawl commenced.

The fight spilled into the main concert room and towards the stage, where the unfortunate Dwight Dazzle was back on stage and performing that well known classic "I'll take you home again Kathleen."

The fight which was in competition with Dwight for attention was winning hands down, but the singer valiantly carried on with his act into the second verse.

On the refrain of "...........take you home Kathleen," the concert secretary unplugged Dwight's microphone from the

159

main socket, plugged in his own and shouted, "Hey up, pack it in now. We're not eving feighting int club. Its Kirkby, not Dodge City."

With that he replaced Dwight's microphone, who continued to sing as though nothing had happened.

"…………yes I'd take you home again………….."

Just then a bottle flew onto the stage and connected with the bingo machine behind Dwight, who had skilfully ducked out of its flight path.

"……..Kathleen."

Although concentrating on his act, he had the wherewithal to lift the microphone stand sufficiently so that a passing bar stool could find its way onto the stage without damaging his sound system. Other little dodges became necessary as a variety of objects joined him on the perilous platform. One object larger than most was Stan the pot bellied man, who had to sit at the foot of the stage during one of his refilling journeys, as his route had been blocked.

The scene began to resemble a John Wayne saloon brawl as other people became involved.

Dwight had lost his battle hands down and despite the concert secretary's constant interruptions the audience had even ceased to show indifference.

"I'll not tell thee agean,," shouted the concert secretary, and indeed he was right, as three brawling men fell against his podium knocking the microphone from his hands. The pipe went again, and the concert secretary reacted in the same way.

"Oh fuck,"

and he was right to exclaim in that manner for the whole place was in uproar.

"and I'll take you to your D'ome againeeeeeee……ow you bastard!" shouted Dwight at the end of his song, as a bar stool hit the side of his head, dislodging his toupee.

The concert secretary had little alternative but to take extreme measures to try to call a halt to the fighting. He did this by shouting to the audience that the Club was going to call a 'free house', which was an extra game of Bingo without charge. Strangely, those few words managed to calm a situation within a quarter of an hour which the riot squad would not have been able to manage had they stayed there all night.

By the end of it, Hedley had swelling to both eyes, a bloody nose and his false teeth had been knocked out, found, and taken home by some lucky reveller. He was led away by some of his acquaintances and went straight to the local police station to file a complaint. Bruce, on the other hand, was relatively unscathed, apart from a bloody nose which was treated by the concert secretary's wife in the gents' toilet.

One visitor raised a slight objection, only to be told by Madge,

"Ger on wi it, its nowt I 'ave'nt seen afore."

"Ha, but tha aint seen this one," said the visitor in reply, and promptly went to face the urinal. However, before he could start Bruce's girlfriend walked into the toilet to check his welfare going straight past the man at the urinal. A few seconds later her sister came in and all three women began asking Bruce how he felt. The man at the urinal gave up and muttering something about coming back later, adjusted his dress and left the toilet.

The 'last house' was then announced by the concert secretary.

"This is last 'ouse for a tenner and who ever wins can buy me a new pipe."

Some wag in the audience shouted, "Bollocks" but the minute the first ball was drawn there was complete silence, as though the battle of gents bog had never occurred.

"Clicketty Click Sixty Six," continued the concert secretary. "All the fours, forty four. Downing Street number 10," and with that the microphone began to react from the rough treatment it had been given earlier in the evening.

"Ucky for some umber…even."

It was interesting that audiences playing bingo demanded complete silence, and there would be much tutting if anyone had the audacity to speak. While this was going on, Dwight Dazzle was putting the covers on his equipment and accidentally knocked over the microphone stand.

With that the Concert Secretary stopped calling the numbers and shouted out to Dwight,

"I'll have no .ruptions when I'm .oing the ……… aller so get off until we've done will tha."

"Argh get off will tha," said somebody in the audience.

"Argh piss off," added another, and with that poor old Dwight left the stage.

Dwight shouted to the concert secretary, "Why don't you close the curtains?" but to no avail as he resumed the game. Dwight indignantly turned to Eric, his mate who helped him with his gear, and said, "Last time I saw curtains like that, was the last time I saw our uncle Ernie." Eric laughed but the concert secretary shouted angrily,

"I've telled thee before, get off."

".op of the shop number ninety……, blind fifty……, blind seventy."

I have never understood why bingo callers refer to numbers as being blind, but as this one spoke his emphasis was on the capital 'B' which made the microphone make a booming sound as he spoke.

"What were that number Eddie?" said the woman with the blue rinse.

"Blind seventy," said her friend.

"Oh, I though he said eighty," said the blue rinse.

"No, seventy," said her friend.

"Ah, seventy," said the concert secretary, who picked up the conversation.

"Can't tha get someone else to mark the card if tha can't .ear."

"Don't you get on at me Harry Goldthorpe," said the blue rinse.

"Get on wi it," said a number of other participants, and with that, two and six, twenty six was called and someone shouted, "'OUSE."

One of the committee men, who was a man in an old tweed suit with a brass watch and chain in his waistcoat, dealer boots, a flat hat and no teeth, strode over to the winner and collected his card before taking it back to the main microphone. This simple task represented the pinnacle of his authority and presence on the world stage. He shouted out the numbers using a chesty voice to its full potential, causing him to cough after every number.

"'OUSE CORRECT," he shouted, and the winner marched to the front of the stage to collect her ten quid.

With that the noise resumed and our pot bellied friend made his twelfth visit from the table to the bar for his refill, nodding to his pal George on route.

Another reveller dashed to the gents looking strained and pale but returning a few minutes later calm and composed.

Half way through the house the police arrived to find a state of complete order. They looked around noticing people with trickles of blood running from their noses and ears but simply wiping it away while absorbed in concentration at the numbers which were being called out. The police decided not to interrupt the game and so they turned round and left without a word.

Bingo is a very serious business in South Kirby, much more serious than fighting.

163

The following morning Bruce was getting ready for work when the local constabulary called at his house. The 'Jam Sandwich' contained two officers, one young and fresh faced and the other old and care worn.

"What's to do Eddie?" said Bruce recognising the older officer as he got out of the car.

"We've come over that feight you had with 'edley Salter tother neet."

"Nay gi ore," said Bruce, "'e cracked me, not me cracked 'im. I 'ad to defend mesen."

"I know," said Eddie, "But he's made a complaint tha sees, so you'll 'ave to come to put your side down. It'll not take long and I'll give you a lift home."

"I'm just on my way to wuk," said Bruce, "I can't afford to miss a shift Eddie, dun't ask me to do that."

"What time do you finish the shift?" said Eddie.

"'Alf four," said Bruce. "Let me get 'ome and showered and I'll come to see ya at half past five."

"OK," said Eddie, "We'll do that, providing you come straight away."

"Fair do's," said Bruce. "Thanks for that Eddie, I'll be there."

As the officers walked away, the younger one spoke.

"Why didn't you nick him straight away Eddie?" he said, "It's a serious charge and we don't have to wait for him to come back from work surely?"

"Correct lad," said Eddie, "But did you want to feight him? And besides, 'e'll turn up, 'e's not going to duck us." PC Eddie was right, for at quarter past five Bruce, as true as his word, presented himself at the Kirby nick.

The interview was completed on the "new fangled tape", but not before PC Eddie had lost the chart explaining how tape recordings should be conducted. Eventually the deed was done and Bruce put his side of the story on record. He denied an assault and claimed that he had acted in self-defence, promising PC Eddie that he would be able to present no less than ten witnesses to support him, one of whom may well have seen the incident in the toilet which started the fight.

The witness was seen and he confirmed Bruce's story. Numerous other witnesses came forward to support what had happened in the concert room, and PC Eddie completed his report and submitted it to his superiors for them to decide if action should be taken. Later that afternoon Bruce, with his faithful dog Goz called into the pub for a quick pint.

At another pub at the far end of town Hedley Salter sat in the tap room nursing his swollen face and bruised ego. In their own ways both men were anxious for the decision as to whether a prosecution would follow or not.

The first week in October Bruce was at home when a police car arrived and a police woman and police cadet marched up to his door carrying a piece of carbonated paper. Bruce answered the door, gave a broad smile to the pretty young police woman and invited them both in. As he stood back in the hallway, he allowed both ladies to walk into his room, giving him the opportunity of inspecting them from the rear. Without giving a thought as to the reason for their visit Bruce, in his usual flirtatious way, invited both ladies to join him in a drink, which they politely declined on the basis that they were on duty.

Bruce was wearing a tight black T shirt which showed off his muscular frame. This was a ploy he had used many times on unsuspecting females and he noticed out of the corner of his eye the young police cadet studying him carefully.

"What can I do for you two young ladies?" asked Bruce. "Just name it," he added, with his most seductive smile.

"Are you Mr Bruce Johnson?" said the police woman.

"That's me luv in the flesh, in person before your very eyes, ready willing and able."

"It's not a social visit Mr Johnson, but I have been instructed to bring you this summons."

Bruce's attitude changed, as did the look on his face.

"What's this about a summons?" said Bruce.

"It's a summons ordering you to attend before the Pontefract Magistrates' Court on the 18th October, charged with an offence of causing actual bodily harm to a man called............" the police officer paused whilst she looked for the name in the charge, "Yes, here it is, Hedley Salter."

Bruce's immediate response was,

"Tha what? Eddie said they would never do me. What's gone off?" He took the summons and read it voraciously, only to be told that there was a second summons alleging that on the same night in the same place his conduct had caused a breach of the peace.

At the other end of the town, PC Eddie and his fresh faced colleague were busy knocking on the door of number 25 carrying out their everyday duties. The row of terraced houses were all the same; the colour scheme, the leaded windows and the same net curtains which hid interested busy bodies who watched as the police car arrived. The windows were empty save for those who watched. The door was answered by a man in his mid thirties, tall and balding, with tobacco stained teeth giving way to a permanent sneer. As the door opened PC Eddie spoke.

"You're Hedley Salter aren't you?"

"Ah, what abart it?" came the reply.

"I'm here to deliver a summons to you Hedley. It requires you to be at the Pontefract Magistrates' Court on the 18th

166

October.   A shocked Hedley Salter took the document and read its contents, speaking the words from the summons:

"That you on the 20th day of August 1983 did assault Bruce Johnson, thereby occasioning actual bodily harm contrary to Section 47 of the Offences Against the Person Act 1861."

Underneath it was a further summons alleging that Hedley had behaved in such a way as his conduct gave rise to a breach of the peace.

"You fucking lousy bastards.   I complain and you fucking summons me.   Well we'll see about this.   Fucking Johnson's got it coming."

"Don't you be doing anything stupid Hedley," said PC Eddie, "'Cos you'll be the first person we'll come looking for."

"Well what about him.   What about him assaulting me?"

"For your information, he'll be receiving a summons for assaulting you round about now.   I advise you to see a solicitor before the 18th, because it's a serious charge.   Have you anything to add?"

PC Eddie had probably made a mistake, because the invitation simply gave Hedley the opportunity to vent his spleen.

"Fuck him, fuck this and fuck you. Now get off my front."

"It's a pleasure," said PC Eddie, "And as they say in the trade, we'll see you in court."

Hedley slammed his door while Eddie and his colleague walked back to the panda car.

Bruce came to see me following a recommendation from a mutual acquaintance.   For the most part, legal representation is regionalised with people choosing their solicitor from those practicing in the town where they live.   However there are a number of defendants who prefer to go out of town, and Bruce was one of them..   He had done the rounds of the local solicitors throughout a career which was littered with offences of minor disorder and drunkenness.   I suppose he thought that going out of the town might change his luck. I found him to be a fairly friendly character and very much a man's man. We hit it off immediately.

Hedley, on the other hand, had chosen the very able services of a local brief to help him fight his corner. And so on the 18th of October 1983 we all appeared at Pontefract Magistrates' Court. It was an old building much in need of repair and, although the staff were pleasant, I was viewed as a foreigner. Unless you are known to the local briefs they too can regard you as an outsider and something of a trespasser on their patch. Fortunately I knew one or two of the advocates so I did not feel too much out of place. However Hedley's representative viewed me with considerable suspicion, and sought me out on my arrival. He asked me what pleas we would be tendering and appeared to be extremely disappointed when I told him we were pleading not out. As we spoke, Bruce and Hedley sat at opposite sides of the room giving each other the dead eye. There was a considerable atmosphere in the court, something which had gained the attention of the court police officer who felt obliged, almost like a referee, to speak to both the defence solicitors.

"We don't want any trouble in here," said PC Arthurs.

"Don't worry we don't intend to fight between us, at least not yet," I replied smiling at Hedley's solicitor.

"I don't mean you two, I mean the defendants," said PC Arthurs. "It's them two," pointing to Hedley and Bruce.

My opposite number took great exception to the police officer speaking to him like a school master to his pupil, and he complained quite vociferously when PC Arthurs returned to his place in the corridor.

"He has absolutely no right to speak to us like that," he said behind PC Arthur's back.

"Quite so," I said, "I think we ought to crack him."

"I beg your pardon," said the solicitor.

"Oh nothing," I said, "It's just the antagonist in me coming out."

We went into the court to seek out the representative of the Crown Prosecution Service, who was a pleasant lady in her forties who was unable to cope with stress in any form.

"I'm sorry, I can't speak to you at the moment, I have just been given five new prisoner files and I haven't read them and I need to speak to the police officers and check some TIC's on another file and then speak to two of my witnesses who have been brought here unnecessarily and not only that I am not feeling very well and shouldn't really be at work but two of my colleagues are already off with stress so I have got to fly the flag", she complained, all in one breath.

It was impossible to get a word in edgeways, so I just said, "Jolly hockey sticks," to myself and took my place on the solicitor's bench. My prosecutor friend spoke again.

"You'll not get on first. There is a large list this morning and some important matters which the clerk will want to call on before you," she said, justifying her unhelpful initial approach. I did not reply and so she repeated herself.

"I'm sorry," I replied, "I can't speak to you now. I have got to consider my client's case and statement and I have got to be back in Rotherham for 11.30a.m. and I have a client outside who is likely to have a fight with his co-accused and then PC Arthurs will tell me off claiming that I am responsible for something I can be entirely unresponsible for if you see what I mean."

The prosecutor just looked at me as though I was from outer space and put her spectacles back on, allowing the silver chain which secured them to dangle from her neck towards her opened bottle of ink.

"Excuse me," I said, and pulled her chain to one side. She gave forth a vitriolic outburst, but could not bring herself to thank me for my intervention. The other solicitors on the bench who had been similarly treated by her earlier were highly amused.

The clerk of the court came out of the magistrates' room and I immediately recognised her as someone who used to work in another court in the area and with whom I got on extremely well.

"Good morning Mr Smith," she said.

"Good morning madam, how nice to see you again," I replied.

"What case have you got Steve?" she asked.

"Johnson and Salter. My friend here represents Salter. We are both pleading not guilty and the matter is to be sent out for a trial."

"Very well," said the clerk, "We'll call that on first."

The prosecutor looked at me with considerable disdain and I just winked at her as our two clients were brought into court.

"I have not read this file," said the prosecutor, but the court clerk was used to her and was not prepared to be messed about.

"But Mr Smith says that this is a not guilty plea so I see no reason why that can't be entered whether you have read it or not."

"Oh very well", said the prosecutor begrudgingly, and then the magistrates walked in.

The chairman of the bench was a lady in her sixties who surveyed the advocates in front of her. She fastened her eyes upon me and realised that she had not seen me before. I got the same vibes from her as I got from the prosecutor. I sensed her thinking, "Who are you and what are you doing here in my court?"

I felt like saying I had just come to read the meter, but I remained silent. I have lots of imaginary conversations when I am sitting in court waiting to deal with my cases.

Bruce and Hedley were standing at least six feet apart and the prosecutor mumbled through her summary so as to allow the magistrates to decide whether they would deal with the case or send it to the crown court.

My colleague and I both argued that summary trial in the magistrates' court was appropriate and to be frank neither of us went into too much detail because it seemed a foregone conclusion. One of the things you learn about magistrates' court work is that nothing is a foregone conclusion and you must never take things for granted.

Much to our surprise the magistrates retired to consider their decision, leaving me to reflect upon Bruce's statement while the bench was out.

Bruce's case was that he thought Hedley was going to attack him, and the law provides a defence to an assault charge in these circumstances. A defendant does not have to wait for an assault to take place before he defends himself. He is quite entitled to act if he believes he is going to be attacked. Thereafter a fight took place during which Bruce had to defend himself or be given a thrashing.

The prosecution were alleging that they had both assaulted each other and during the fight their conduct breached the peace. It is not unusual for the prosecution to "back both horses" in cases such as this, to allow the defendants to fight it out amongst themselves in a trial.

A way of dealing with such cases was to bind both protagonists over to keep the peace, and I suggested this course to the prosecutor. I had had the opportunity of seeing the prosecution evidence, and to be fair it was not clear just who was guilty of assault, but a breach of the peace was

171

implicit from what had happened in the concert room. It was a straight clash of evidence between Bruce and Hedley and it would be a matter of whom the court believed.

I put the suggestion of a bind over again but the prosecutor would not even consider it.

The bench returned and agreed summary trial. Both defendants pleaded not guilty, but before the case was adjourned, I informed the court that a bind over was on offer. The clerk expressed the view that it was a good idea if both parties agreed and invited the prosecutor to comment. Unfortunately she had not been listening and very much to my surprise, she said so. The Clerk was not impressed and she said so. The bench suggested an adjournment so she could consider her position, but she protested that it was not her file and asked for an adjournment to let the reviewing lawyer make a decision.

The case was adjourned for a month and the parties left court. The following day I heard from Hedley's solicitor that his client was not prepared to be bound over and was determined to proceed with his complaint of assault.

Over the next few weeks, Bruce continued with his life working most days and going on his evening jog with the ever faithful dog 'Goz'. Goz was a whippet and Jack Russell cross. It was a peculiar looking but affectionate animal who followed Bruce about with complete devotion. On one such run Bruce was crossing the common when he was spotted by Hedley Salter who was driving by.

Following a further court appearance, the CPS agreed to drop all the charges providing each defendant agreed to be bound over. When we attended at court I discussed the proposition with Bruce. He was agreeable to the suggested course, but Hedley was far from happy because it meant that the assault charge which he had brought against Bruce would be dropped.

172

It was good advice to be bound over and Hedley's solicitor had been at pains to tell him so, but we often find that defendants know best and prefer to chart their own course. Too much pressure can result in alienation from the client, so it is a tricky path to tread to get it right and try to suit all parties.

The day was won, however, because Hedley had recent convictions and he feared that if he was found guilty of assault he may be sent to prison. With the utmost regret he confirmed his agreement to be bound over.

Hedley's solicitor and I agreed that the best way to deal with the case was to avoid entering into a slanging match between us, so the decision was taken to adopt a 'least said soonest mended' approach.

After we had both finished addressing the bench, both of them were bound over in the sum of £100.00 for one year and all the charges were dismissed. Hedley was unhappy with the result and made the complaint to his solicitor that he had been the person who was assaulted and yet he had been given the same treatment as his assailant. As we were walking out of the court, Hedley turned to Bruce and said, "You'll pay for this" and he meant it.

Fortunately, Bruce did not reply, otherwise I was convinced we would have had another punch up. As we left the court, I saw that Hedley was waiting outside. I toyed with the idea of remaining inside with Bruce until Hedley had gone, but Bruce was quite unperturbed and when we got outside, Hedley repeated his threat, but was ushered away by his solicitor.

I dropped Bruce off in South Kirkby but declined to join him for a pint, saying that I was wearing my best suit and was without my body armour. Bruce laughed and we shook hands and I drove off in search of the council building in York where I was to appear for a client on a Criminal Injuries

Compensation Board appeal. I got there with ten minutes to spare to find that I was the seventh case on the list and they were still dealing with the first one. I need not have driven like a maniac or sworn at that JCB drivers on the way. The words "deary, deary me" (or something similar) came to mind as I sat among a bevy of injured victims, dissatisfied with their awards.

At 5.00 p.m. and despite my protestations, our case had still not been reached and at 5.05 p.m. I was told that the Board were not prepared to sit beyond quarter past and I would have to come back another day. The words "deary, deary me" came to mind yet again as I faced the hard slog down the A1 back to Rotherham.

That night when Bruce went to his dog's kennel in the yard to take Goz for his evening run, he was surprised to find that the dog was not in its pen, yapping incessantly with excitement at the prospect of his daily exercise. He opened the gate to find poor Goz laid lifeless in a corner. A piece of half eaten meat lay at the dog's side, the smell of which gave Bruce a positive clue as to what had happened.

Goz was dead! He had been poisoned.

Chapter Ten

INGROWING TOENAILS AND BRUCE'S REVENGE

Although the regular Wednesday evening football match was one of the highlights of my week, I found it increasingly difficult to get there on time.   Long lists of appointments following lengthy appearances in the magistrates' court were beginning to stretch my working days into the evenings.   My life began to resemble one long series of races from one place to another, and so it was as 1983 moved towards autumn.

No matter what the weather, we would play football be it in scorching sun or bitterly cold winds.   Even if there was snow, we still played in track suits so that the ice would not cut our flesh when the inevitable collisions occurred or Bader Lidster would accidentally kick you up the arse.

However I had major problems with my big toes for both had been broken in my pursuit of footballing excellence and an ingrowing toe nail gave me a great deal of discomfort.   When I used my toes to kick a heavy ball, the pain was excruciating. The condition deteriorated so much so that in the end I sought the services of a local chiropodist.

My first visit had been fixed for Tuesday morning, the day before the match.   I was limping quite badly, with both toes swollen and extremely tender.   I even had difficulty pulling on socks, such was the pain.

I arrived at the chiropodists and walked into the waiting room which was a 'museum' dedicated to 1950's decor.

There were photographs and pictures all the way round the room of diseased feet in all manner of shapes and sizes and in varying states of decay.   The only other patient waiting was an extremely large woman with the most offensive looking left foot I had ever seen in my life.   Her foot was on a stool and was so red and angry looking that sparks appeared to be given off at intervals from the verruca laden foot,

"You can go before me luv, I'm early," said the woman, obligingly. "You wouldn't believe that I used to be a dancer would you?"

"No, I wouldn't," I thought to myself, but I didn't want to cause offence so I just smiled and nodded,

"Just look at my toe," she said, "You will see what real pain is about."

I declined her kind offer, saying that I had just had a sandwich but I believed every word she said,

"Now, look, and I will show you what I mean," she insisted.

I have never been able to understand people's preoccupation with illness, pain and discomfort and the desire for everyone to share in it. Despite my obvious reluctance she kept insisting that I give her foot an inspection and present a prognosis.

"Yes, I can see it from here," I said moving as far away as possible.

Fortunately, I was rescued by the chiropodist who called me into his consulting room. As I walked in the lady disturbed me by raising her eyes to the ceiling almost as a warning.

The chiropodist was an old man, I guessed between sixty-five and seventy. His back was bowed, doubtless by all the years of bending over and dealing with feet. He had a gaunt appearance and appeared to be suffering from either liver trouble or Chinese ancestry. His fingers were extremely long and thin but the most disturbing thing about him was his bottle bottom glasses, which did not seem to help him as much as they should. He was continually bumping into objects and knocking them over, each time making the weary comment,

"Oh deary, deary me."

He motioned me to sit on his consulting chair, which had a small stool in front of it used for resting the feet, and to take off my shoes and socks. He cleaned his glasses, replaced them, and again invited me to sit down.

"I am sitting down," I said in surprise.

"Oh, of course you are, splendid. Now then, what can I do for you madam?"

All the confidence I had in him left at that moment. In my attempt to avoid causing embarrassment, I spoke in as deep a voice as I could.

"It's these two big toes, I have ingrowing toe nails in both and I am in a terrific amount of pain."

I thought that would give him sufficient clue as to my gender and my problem.

"Oh deary, deary me," he replied, "Ingrowing toe nails can be very nasty and if they go septic it can lead to all sorts of problems. You do remember the story of Douglas Bader the fighter pilot don't you?"

I did remember the story and I didn't appreciate the reminder.

"Let's have a look and see what we can do," he continued.

I looked in horror as he lifted his glasses away from his eyes and stared at my feet, which I had put on the stool in front of me. As he fumbled towards me, he accidentally struck my right big toe. No sooner than I was off the ceiling and back in the chair, he decided he would examine the offending toes with his long thin fingers. I was soon on the ceiling again, reminding him that I was in considerable pain.

"Well you would be," said the chiropodist, "There is nothing worse than ingrowing toe nails. They can be extremely painful." For some reason the name 'arse hole' came to mind. I looked away as I couldn't bear to watch the operation and so I concentrated upon a number of certificates for miscellaneous qualifications in chiropody hanging on the wall.   Before long, I was on the ceiling again.   I am not generally squeamish, but my anguish was so intense that I suggested there might be some way of freezing the foot so as to eliminate some of the pain.

"What a good idea," he said, reaching out for some spray.

He coated my foot with wasp killer before finding a soothing antiseptic numbing spray.   I was protected against pain and any marauding wasps and in an instant I was completely numb below my knees.   He then set about his work with relish, though still I could not bear to look.

I thought I saw the sight of blood at one stage, but by the time I plucked up the courage to look more closely he had mopped up whatever I had lost.   Finally he appeared to have finished. "Thank God!"   I thought to myself, but my relief was short lived.

"Right, now I will do your other foot," said my tormentor.

"Oh Christ!" I replied, staring up at the ceiling in readiness for my next visit.

Despite the anti-freeze dispensed about my lower limbs, the pain was still intense, and I began to sweat profusely.

"Oh deary, deary me, this little bugger is being awkward," said the old man in continued ignorance of my waning confidence.

"He certainly is," I replied referring to another little bugger.

As I closed my eyes, I visualised him going about his work in a Gestapo officer's uniform complete with swastika arm band. If he had asked me to divulge my inner most secrets, I would have done so for the promise of an end to the torment.

After what seemed like an eternity of torture, he had finished. He stood in triumph holding a piece of blood stained nail with a pair of tweezers.

"Got him!" he exclaimed in triumph.   "I think you will find that your problems are over for the time being."

"The time being?" I queried.

"Yes, I'm afraid they will grow back in the same way. You'll need the treatment again," he said with a grin.

"Bloody hell," was all I could think of to say.

"How do you feel now?" asked the chiropodist.

"I haven't felt like this since I was in Dachau," I replied sarcastically.

"Splendid," said my torturer.

I attempted to move, but the magic spray had not worn off. As I tried to stand my legs gave way and I fell, landing with my face in the plastic container which housed the day's collection of other people's toe nails, verrucas and dead skin.

All dignity long since removed, I staggered to my feet and wobbled out like a drunken man to be greeted by the woman with the rotting foot.

"Did it hurt love?" she asked.

"Not at all," I said, wiping the sweat from my face and neck.

The lady patient then hobbled into the consulting room. As the door closed the only words I could hear were "Deary, deary me."

As I left by the stairs I could have sworn I heard someone on the ceiling.

By the time I had got back to the office, the effects of the magic spray had worn off and my toes were throbbing unmercifully. I paused at the top of the stairs to be greeted with the sound of a trombone. The office toilet was occupied by one of Jarvis's staff, the Honourable Oscar, horse racing specialist and all round good egg.

"Hello Oscar," I shouted.

"Hello Steve. Hey the 3.30 at Kelso, Chipmunks Chum, good odds 5 - 1 soft going, its got a shout."

"How much of a shout?" I asked.

"A good un, a fivers worth", said Oscar.

179

"OK, a fiver it is, will you put it on?"

"OK, and with that the flush went and Oscar appeared in all his glory with a toilet roll in one hand and The Racing News in the other.

"I always take my own," said Oscar, anticipating my question.

"The Racing News?" I queried.

"No, the bog roll," he said.

"There's nothing worse than getting in there and finding there isn't one."

"A toilet roll?" I asked.

"No, The Racing News!" said Oscar. "I have to have complete quiet to study the form."

"Complete quiet?" I queried.

"Aye, it's the only place where you can get it round here," he said.

"You could have fooled me, it's the noisiest place in the building when you are in it," I countered.

Oscar either didn't hear, or else chose not to, and began to walk into his office. He paused before entering.

"A fiver then?"

"A fiver," I replied. And with that he was gone.

I limped into the reception where Wilf was opening the post.

"You're limping like an old man," said Wilf.

"I've just had my toes done." I replied seeking sympathy.

Just then, Mrs Mott joined us.

"He's limping like an old man," said Wilf.

"Terrible thing that gout," said Mrs Mott.

"I beg your pardon?" I asked.

"Gout is a terrible thing, makes you limp like an old man. My father had it, it killed him you know, dead.....killed him, dead, dead, dead.."

"Gout can't kill," I said.

"It killed him, he tried to cross the road but he was too slow."

"And…?" I asked earnestly.

"A lorry ran him over!! If it hadn't been for the gout, he would have got out of the way. Mind you, he never felt a thing, so they say……..So you want to watch that. It's a killer gout is. Cup of tea Mr Smith?"

"Yes please," I replied, shaking my head.

"Have you any anti-gout pills?" asked Wilf.

"No, but I've got some senna pods. They'll clean your system out," replied Mrs Mott. "That's what you need, a proper clearout," she continued.

"It's only ingrowing toe nails, Mrs Mott," I protested pointlessly.

"Aye senna pods…………good clearout, yes, good clearout that'll do it."

"What about my ingrowing toe nails?" I queried but before she could answer, Mrs Mott had disappeared.

"Marvellous," I announced, "She'll tell the bloody world I've got gout now, and that she has recommended a good clearout. I hope she doesn't tell Pagey."

"Killed her father that," said Wilf, solemnly.

"Bugger off," I replied and limped into my room. I realised my attempts to gain sympathy had fallen on stoney ground.

I had various letters to answer and quite a bit of junk mail to throw across at the waste bin. It was a little contest I had with myself each morning. I was fairly accurate, but that afternoon I failed on all three throws. It was a bad omen.

As I was busy dictating, the telephone rang.

"Pontefract police on the line for you," said Tracey.

"Pontefract police, what do they want?"

"Don't know, sounds urgent."

"Hello, Steve Smith speaking.

"Good afternoon Mr Smith, Sergeant Tindall, Pontefract police, I'm ringing to see if you can help us?"

"What's the problem?"

"I understand that you act for Bruce Johnson of South Kirkby."

"I did," I replied, "But his case finished nearly a month ago."

"Well, he might be contacting you. We have been looking for him, and he knows it. We thought he might try to reach you."

"What's going on? What's happened?" I asked.

"The night before last there was an incident near a South Kirkby public house. A man called Hedley Salter was involved in a fight. He was knocked unconscious and suffered head injuries. He died on his way to hospital and we believe your client Bruce Johnson was responsible. We are anxious to interview him."

I felt guilty, as though the police thought I was concealing something, and the more I protested I knew nothing, the more guilty I felt.

"I'm afraid there's nothing I can do sergeant. He may have made other arrangements and seen someone else. There's nothing more I can add, but if he contacts me I will certainly be prepared to advise him," I said forcefully.

"I hope you will get him to hand himself in. We wouldn't want you to stick your neck out would we?"

"No we wouldn't," I said, refusing to grab the bait. I put the telephone down, thinking what an ignorant sod the sergeant was, but I couldn't help thinking about Bruce. What if he had killed him? But then he may have already made other arrangements to see another solicitor so I put the matter to the back of my mind.

The rest of the day passed quickly. I saw a long list of appointments, before calling it a day at almost 6.00pm. Wilf had gone earlier and the office was empty. It was very quiet and by the time I packed my brief case with a few files and set off for home there was no-one about.

I locked the doors after turning out all the lights, but I had a feeling that I was being watched.

There were some bushes growing near to the office which looked out over a grassed area, leading to the paths which surrounded the church. They were most pleasant during the day but quite eerie at night. The bushes rustled in the breeze and I stopped for a second, without turning to look. Just then I heard a voice:

"Mr Smith," and again, "Mr Smith."

I looked around, but could see no one, until I studied the bushes closely. I began to walk towards the sound.

"Who is it?" I asked.

"It's me, Bruce, Bruce Johnson from Kirkby. Look I need to speak to you, urgent like. I can't speak to you through the bushes, but they are looking for me. Look! In your office please, you go in, I'll follow, just for a few minutes please. Are you on your own?"

"OK Bruce," I said, walking back to the office door.

"Everyone has gone."

Unlocking it, I stepped inside, and almost immediately Bruce was there. He was dirty and unkempt, looking every bit like a man on the run. He glanced from side to side as if expecting to be discovered at any second. He spoke somewhat breathlessly.

"Can we go inside?"

"Of course," I replied, and walked up the stairs.

"The police are looking for me," said Bruce.

"I know," I replied.

"How?" he asked.

"They rang me this afternoon, thinking you might have contacted me."

"Christ, are they watching your office?"

"I doubt it, I told them I hadn't seen you.   They can't watch everywhere you might call."

"I'm sorry," said Bruce," I shouldn't have come, but I didn't know where to turn."

"What happened?"

"Well, Hedley and me have been sort of against each other since that court case and he never forgave me for getting off. Then he killed my dog, he poisoned him.   It was an 'orrible thing to do.   That dog never hurt anyone.   Well, I went looking for 'im, but didn't catch 'im until Monday night.   I saw him outside the local, so I pulled up in the car and challenged him about it.   We had a fight, well not a fight really.   He went for me first so I defended myself.   I didn't want to fight.   I only hit him once and he went down.   That's all I did honest, I didn't do anything else.   I tried to bring him round, but he was out.

I propped him up and buggered off.   I was sure he would be OK.   It wasn't natural.   It was as if he was out before he went down.   I then heard he had died.   I panicked and ran off.   I got some things and left.   I've borrowed a mate's car, 'cos the police know my registration number, and I've just driven around laying low during the day.   They are trying to get me for murder!!"

Bruce was terrified.   For all he was a man's man, fearless and worried about no one, that evening he was a trembling, frightened man like a rat in a trap.

"What do I do?" asked Bruce.

There was really only one reply I could make.

"You've got to hand yourself in.   Sooner or later they will catch you and it won't look good if they have had to fetch you."

"Then what?" asked Bruce anxiously.

184

"Then we prepare our case."

"Oh aye, while I'm inside. Brilliant."

"I don't think you will get bail, but there's always a chance," I continued.

"Always a chance eh, aye one in a million."

"But where else are you going to go?"

"I might get out of the country."

"Then what? And how will you live?"

"I'll find a way," said Bruce pathetically.

"They will be watching every port and airport. You won't get out, and by then you will look guilty."

Bruce thought for a moment before speaking again.

"But they won't believe me," he implored

"Why not?" I asked. Are you sure you only hit him once?"

"Yes."

"Are you sure, you know they can make forensic checks?"

"I'm sure. I just can't explain it, it wasn't even a punch. I didn't really connect."

"Alright, tell me why you hit him."

"Because he was going to hit me............."

"Well there's no one to go against it if there are no witnesses."

"There was no one, there was only us there."

"Then why not tell the police just that?"

"They won't believe me."

"Why not?"

Bruce would not answer. He was right to look on the black side, but he needed to be realistic. In this particular instance there was only one thing to do, and that was to give himself up and explain what had happened.

"Will you come with me?" he asked.

"Of course, and I'll stay for the interview and then we will try for bail. The first thing we want to know about is the post mortem."

"What's that?"

"It's the official medical examination of the body to find the cause of death. We can get our own opinion as well."

Bruce took a deep breath, the indications were that he was having second thoughts.

I tried to re-enforce what I had already said.

"Sooner or later they will get you. There is no advantage to stay on the run. The police will want to know why you didn't hand yourself in and they will think you have got something to hide."

"Well I have," replied Bruce, "He's dead for God's sake, and I did it!"

"Yes, but according to you, you acted in self defence. There is no-one to dispute what you say!" I repeated his defence case.

"They will put me inside, I just can't stand the thought of prison."

Just then the big man started to cry. I've seen so many of the so called hard men fold up like a pack of cards when prison was mentioned, for there are very few who embrace the prison gates with affection.

As Bruce began to regain his composure he spoke out,

"I'll give myself up, but I've got something I need to do first."

"OK, it suits me, I've got to go to court in the morning. I'll be finished by about noon. I'll meet you at Pontefract police station at quarter to one. I'll ring the police tomorrow morning and tell them you are coming in."

"You will come won't you?" asked Bruce pathetically.

"Yes," I replied, "I'll be there, but don't have me on a wild goose chase. I'll see you at quarter to one. Don't say anything to the police until I arrive."

Bruce nodded in grim acceptance and then set off into the night and to goodness knows where.

The following day I went to court early. I wanted to be finished as soon as I could, but my luck was out. Everything went well until 11.30am. One client had not attended and the court had issued a bench warrant, but in true style he turned up late to ruin my morning.

"They have issued a bench warrant," I said to Terry Truelove.

"Sorry Steve but I overlaid," said Mr Truelove, a man of few words with a hare lip and shocking wind. Terry was light fingered and could not keep his hands off other people's property. He had chosen to visit Silverwood Colliery pit stack arriving with a number of thick plastic sacks for the filling thereof.

Terry had a number of customers who he kept supplied with fuel while they kept him in beer money. Terry liked a drink, but owing to difficulties with his digestive tract, a big 'session' as he called it played havoc with everyone else.

The problem was that there was a queue to get cases on and the magistrates had retired to consider another case. They had taken some little time to arrive at a decision and I and several other solicitors found that clicking our heels on what we were paid for 'waiting time' was causing more stress than doing the job itself. I watched them all as they fingered their watches nervously as if waiting for the VAT man to call.

Just then the bell rang from the magistrates' retiring room. One bell was for the clerk which meant that the magistrates required his assistance. Our clerk that day was Geoff Clarke, with whom I had forged an understanding. Geoff was very experienced and I used to bother him with my queries when I wasn't sure of the law or what to do.

"Hurry them up Mr Clarke," I pleaded, "I've got to be in Pontefract by 1.00pm."

"You shouldn't take so much on," said Clarkey, "Pontefract's not your area."

"I know, but it's a murder," I said in the hope of some sympathy.

"You can't rush a bench," said Geoff, "murder or no murder."

And of ocurse he was right but that did not help me.

One of the other solicitors protested because he was wanted at the police station where one of his clients was waiting for interview, and another because he had a free luncheon at the expense of a local building society.

Eventually the bench returned and there was a considerable flurry as four solicitors jostled for position on the front bench. Only one case could be called on at a time so three of us were going to be disappointed, and I was one of them.

Sometimes you want to swear in open court, but it is not advisable despite the temptation.

I left the Court at 12.30pm, which allowed me fifteen minutes to travel the fifteen miles or so to Pontefract. It was a stressful journey as I was caught up in traffic and for part of the way I seemed to be following an endless queue of heavy lorries and one Danish sightseer who did not know how to get his hire car out of second gear.

I arrived at Pontefract police station at 1.05pm in a state of high stress to find an empty waiting room. The police had either taken Bruce into custody or he had not bothered to turn up and I had made a journey for nothing.

I rang the counter bell and after a minute or so the office door opened and a large and very manly policewoman appeared at the desk.

She spoke with a deep growl and in a most intimidating fashion.

"Yes," said the policewoman, clearly annoyed by my presence.

"I am Steve Smith, solicitor from Rotherham, and I have........."

"Who?" came the reply.

"Steve Smith."

"Where from?" she continued.

"Rotherham," I replied.

"And what can I do for you?"

"I have an appointment with my client Bruce Johnson who is to be interviewed in relation to a murder allegation."

My comment caught her somewhat by surprise.

"Murder?" she asked.

"Yes, murder," and I then smiled.

"Sit down and I'll check," she said discourteously.

She left the room with a sigh, leaving me in the waiting room feeling most guilty for having bothered her.

A couple of minutes later she returned.

"You're late," she said rather curtly.

"Yes, I know I am," I said even more curtly.

"Well sit down.   They'll be with you in a minute, they're booking your client in now."

"Thank you," I said.

Bruce's main concern was when he was going to get out and so I tried to set up the interview with the police as soon as possible.

Unfortunately, for whatever reason, they were not available and had disappeared to do some enquiries, but quite what they were I have no idea.   I had the option to either sit and wait in the waiting room 'ad infinitum' or disappear.   The difficulty was that no-one had the authority to release Bruce and despite my protests the CID were 'not contactable'.

I explained the position to Bruce who understood perfectly and simply asked me to fetch him a newspaper so he could at least have something to do whilst he waited.

I left the police station saying that I was contactable at the office providing that I had not had to go out on something else for further enquiries. The sergeant took the point and off I went.

As I drove through Pontefract I looked up my old mate Chris Good and suggested that he skive an hour off work and buy me a pint. He did so and bought me two to be exact together with a rather dodgy looking pasty that had seen better days.

When I got back to the office I found a list of messages, including one from someone who had sounded drunk and complained bitterly that we had not been to clean his windows for at least a fortnight. I shouted through to Wilf to see if he had still got his window cleaning round, but his contribution was merely to suggest that I should leave the office straight away and commit a sexual act with a giraffe.

I ventured into the waiting room to see Tracey, who was wearing the latest creation, a purple mini-skirt with purple boots and a peculiar cap, which had clearly been made for somebody else.

Tracey was a very attractive girl and had the ability to look smart in anything. She was slim and with dark brown eyes which smiled joyously when she spoke. She had however, an unusual personality and you didn't really know when to take her seriously. Nevertheless she was extremely popular with staff and clients alike.

"That's an unusual colour Tracey," I suggested.

"What colour?" asked Tracey, somewhat taken aback.

"The purple of your skirt and top."

"It's not purple," said Tracey, "It is Moldavian Blue."

"Oh," I replied, "Are there any more messages for me?"

"Yes," said Tracey, "There are two there sticking out of the diary."

"Which diary?" I asked.

"The red one," replied Tracey.

"Do you mean the Lithuanian pink one?" I said smiling.

"No, the red diary," said Tracey, "With the messages sticking out."

Just then the telephone rang and she answered it in her usual bright and breezy way.

"Wilford Smith & Co."

There was a slight pause and then I heard her say,

"But I am afraid that we don't clean windows. I think you must have got the wrong number..........and the same to you," said Tracey, slamming down the phone.

She stared at me and smiled that broad smile of hers and asked,

"Anything else?"

"No Miss," I replied, "I am alright for the moment."

"Very good," said Tracey, "Well get about your work now."

"Certainly," I said and walked off.

I went into Wilf's room and he was considering a litre bottle of wine. It was an Italian red called Lambrusco. I had not tried the wine before and had a fancy for it. Wilf poured me a tumbler full and we considered it together.

I took the glass and sniffed the concoction.

"Very fruity," I said with the nose of a connoisseur.

I enjoyed the drink very much and so Wilf poured me another, and then another, and before we knew it we had finished the bottle.

It was a brilliant new discovery and one that we were going to add to our wine list.

The down side with Lambrusco is that if you drink a lot of it, it can have a rather laxative effect if you are not too careful.

Wilf had not been careful and the effect was assured. Within the hour the new concoction was withdrawn from our wine list.

At 5.25pm just before the telephones were switched off, I received a call from the Pontefract police. I was told that

Bruce would be interviewed at 5.45pm which would allow me approximately 20 minutes to travel the distance from Rotherham to Pontefract. The journey would normally take about 40 minutes. I would be unable therefore to comply with their time schedules.

I did ask why I had not been given more notice, but at that time solicitors were thought of as being rather a hindrance to enquiries.

I set off straight away but I was convinced that I had got stuck behind the same lorries that had hindered my trip earlier in the day.

I eventually arrived at Pontefract at about 6.30pm to find that the police had gone off for their evening break.

It is not unusual in murder cases for the defence to commission an independent pathologists report. Sometimes it is possible to arrange for the defence pathologist to prepare a report in conjunction with the prosecution expert, and in our case we were lucky because the autopsy had been delayed for one reason or another.

I had instructed Professor Mike Gilchrist from Bradford to act for us and luckily he was available on the afternoon of the interview. The police were so confident that they had a detected murder on their hands, that they fixed the interview to coincide with the autopsy itself. I understood their point and it looked very much as though they were right.

It suited us all.

The idea was that a preliminary interview would take place whilst the autopsy was being carried out and the results would then be considered and a further interview would follow. Professor Gilchrist had an excellent reputation. I had worked with him before and I was happy to work with him again. He had arrived at the Pontefract police station earlier that afternoon. When the police returned, there was a preliminary interview with Bruce and he maintained the same story which he had explained to me. The interview only lasted a matter of a few minutes and was adjourned pending the results of the autopsy.

I had travelled a very short distance to the Pontefract hospital to meet Professor Gilchrist so that I could hear for myself what his opinion was.

He was a very tall man with a shock of grey hair and the look about him of a 'mad professor'. He was extremely intense and devoted to his profession, something which gave him a ready made clientele in the legal profession.

He embarked upon his duty with a considerable vigour, something which shook the majority of us with somewhat queasy stomachs.

I was invited into a small room within the hospital complex where I waited with my briefcase and notebook for the good doctor's arrival.

He entered with a spring in his step. He was a man of some sixty years, who despite his rather grizzly job had retained a considerable youthful look about him. I studied his face carefully and saw a man who spent his life dealing with death and finding out the reasons for it.

As a medical man I suppose he would see life laid bare with all its frailties and complications. He was also party to the results of the seamier side of life, but for some reason best known to him, he enjoyed it.

He stared at me through bright blue eyes over horn-rimmed glasses and studied me before speaking.

"Well, I have seen the deceased and have made a cursory inspection, but I can see no exterior visible signs of injury that would have caused death, so I'm going to consider the question of the heart and also the brain."

I gulped.

"You can remain present during the autopsy if you wish," he said casually.

I looked at him and I looked at the coroner's officer who was looking at me with a grin which meant, 'Have you got the bottle for this old boy'.

I did not have the bottle and so I waited outside.

The autopsy took about an hour, and at the end of it the professor came into the waiting room where I was sitting. His green smock was blood splattered and I was tempted to call him 'Professor Frankenstein'.

He was concentrating heavily on his findings when he addressed me.

"You'll be pleased to know it's an aneurysm resulting from the weakening of the wall due to a variety of possible causes. Loss of elasticity and contractability due to a deficiency in the media is the most important factor.

I looked at him as though he was speaking to me in Greek, and I should add that I cannot speak Greek. My jaw dropped further as he continued:

"Sometimes the arteries at the base of the brain develop a weakness in their walls as a result of natural disease. When the blood is pumped through them, and especially if the blood pressure is raised, these defects cause a progressive weakening of the wall, and the artery develops a bleb, rather like a bubble in bubble gum. This weakened area is known as an aneurysm, and once it has formed one of two things can happen. Firstly, blood may form a clot, layer upon layer, within the aneurysm, so that the defect is sealed up within the lining of the blood vessel. This method of repair virtually restores the normal flow of blood through the artery. However if this compensatory mechanism does not take place the aneurysm is at risk of rupturing, causing a massive haemorrhage to occur at the base of the brain. Death may result immediately from this catastrophe, or it may be delayed for a variable period of time.

One of the factors which may cause the aneurysm to burst is a sudden increase in blood pressure. This surge could be the result of a burst of physical or emotional activity. On the other hand, it must be said, a rupture of such an aneurysm may occur at any time, even if the person is at rest or asleep.

The legal aspect of causation can be complex in these cases. It could be argued that the physical and emotional outburst generated by the confrontation could have raised the blood pressure which precipitated the fatal outcome, without a single blow being struck. On the other hand, knowing that the rupture could have happened at any time, would make it impossible to prove beyond doubt that the alleged assault had anything to do with the death. Once the wall starts to stretch, the process is usually progressive under normal or abnormal hypertensive pressure forces with increasing thinning of the wall until eventual rupture may occur. Build-up of the laminated thrombus within the lumen of the aneurysmal sac is protective but only rarely is this process sufficient to repair the defect and reconstitute a normal lumen to the artery of origin."

My jaw dropped even further with the realisation that I hadn't got a clue what he was talking about. I listened in complete awe as he continued.

"The purely descriptive terms of the macroscopic types which I've mentioned give no idea of the underlying process responsible, and thus a classification largely based on aetiology is more satisfactory."

The good professor looked at me for a reaction. My reaction was more of a man who'd just been told that he had to have an operation for piles.

I took the bull by the horns and spoke.

"What do you mean exactly?"

The Professor repeated every word, a little more slowly than before.

"Oh yes," I said thoughtfully, "In actual fact what you are really saying is that he died of er.........." I looked at him for inspiration and the look on his face made it quite clear that he had realised he was dealing with a complete clot.

"Brain haemorrhage," he said forcefully. "A congenital defect of the media in the angles formed by the junctions of vessels. In other words, particularly with hyper-tension, this area of weak artery stretches and forms what we call an aneurysm, which is where the vessel wall is breached and blood leaks out of it into the skull, causing death."

I was a little happier with that and with the threat of the pile operation being removed, I proceeded to ask some more clot-type questions.

"Could it have been a blow to the head which caused it?" I asked.

"Oh yes, that is a possibility, but I would rather suspect in this case, particularly noting that there were no exterior injuries to the head of any note, that this was purely and simply a case of a brain haemorrhage. Looking at the condition of the brain, it could have happened at any time. The deceased I am afraid to say, was simply living on borrowed time. If it didn't happen then, it could have happened that afternoon, the following day or the following week, but it was certainly going to happen at some time. With the first bleed untreated, sixty percent die, twenty percent are disabled and twenty percent recover."

"If you are able to treat it, what do you do?"

"Well, it is a treatment by direct attack or tying the corotid artery considerably improves the prognosis. For example there is about a twenty-five percent immediate mortality of the survivors, but seventy-five percent are alive, well and at work five years later. This man quite simply and plainly was dying.

It's a very interesting condition, rather akin to that of cirsoid aneurysms which are a mass of dilated elongated pulsating and inter-communicating arteries and veins. More like bags of worms".

I considered what he had said and starting thinking about the pile operation again.

Seeing that I was a little uncomfortable, the professor gave me his conclusion.

"It is my opinion and the opinion of the professor representing the police, that your client's conduct did not contribute to the death.

As I left the hospital I couldn't help wondering what they did with the bits which have been removed during an autopsy. I shuddered to think, and tried to get it out of my mind and headed for my car.

The professor joined us in the car park. He had changed into a smart dark suit which gave him the look of a solicitor. He was tall, slim and very distinguished with horn-rimmed spectacles and an air of sanctimonious indifference. I couldn't help thinking why I couldn't look like that.

I felt his fine bony fingers, rather like those of an artist, as I shook his clammy hand. The thoughts of where they had just been sent another shudder down my spine.

"Looks like you are on to a winner this time Mr Smith," said the professor.

"Looks like it," I said, "But you never know."

"Oh, I rather think you're out on this one," he said confidently. "My colleague for the Crown agrees with my findings and he's talking to the police now."

"Well thank you professor, I am most grateful."

As he turned to go he spoke again.

"Oh by the way there is the question of my bill?"

"Certainly," I replied, "You've got my address?

"Yes, of course. 'Bye for now then, until the next one."

It may seem strange that professionals deal with death in such a matter of fact way but there really is no option and someone has to do it. I felt that sometimes my job is bad enough but dealing with autopsies is something else. I certainly couldn't eat after just watching something like that but most pathologists can eat before and after and even during an autopsy.

The police were disappointed. The medical evidence proved that first impressions and suspicions are not always right. However, the police were still keen to interview Bruce, but not before I had told him the news.

I saw him in a rather pokey Victorian cell which couldn't have been more than ten feet by six feet, in the Pontefract police station. It was antiquated and stank of stale body odour and vomit lingering from days gone by. There was a chill as I entered the cell and I noticed the only furniture was a wooden bed, the frame of which was covered in names carved into the surface.

Bruce was a sorry sight. I put him out of his misery straightaway.

"You didn't kill him Bruce," I said, "It was a brain haemorrhage."

"It was a what?" asked Bruce incredulously.

"It was a brain haemorrhage, as simple as that, and the pathologist seems to think that you did nothing to contribute to the cause of death."

Bruce slumped back on the wooden bed, accidentally banging his head upon the wall.

It was as if five years disappeared from his brow in an instant. All he could say was "Thank God. You say it was a brain haemorrhage?" asked Bruce.

"Yes an aneurysm actually, it's as a result of the weakening of the wall due to a variety of causes. Loss of elasticity and contractability due to a deficiency in the media is the most important factor," I said, implying the knowledge of an expert.

"Eh," said Bruce implying that he hadn't a clue what I was on about.

"Never mind, that's the end of the technicals."

Bruce paused for a short time and spoke again.

"I didn't want him to die, I really didn't...."

"I know you didn't," I replied, "I know."

For the first time Bruce seemed to show a flicker of regret. It brought us both to our senses. After all a life had been lost no matter what he was like or how he used it.

Bruce thought for a minute and then he spoke in a question.

"What will happen to me now?"

"They will want to interview you just to have your account on paper," I said, "And then I rather suspect you will be released."

"Will I be charged with anything?" said Bruce.

"You may be charged with a breach of the peace, but I rather doubt it, as it does not appear that you had actually offended anybody at the time with your behaviour. My advice to you therefore in this instance, is to refuse to answer any questions."

I made this decision because the police had no account of the incident from Bruce and nothing to dispute it and so they would be left with no option but to release him. The equation was clear. He had to keep tight-lipped and leave it at that, and that was the best advice I could give him at the time.

Whether it was right or whether it was wrong was not a consideration, but my duty was to represent him to the best of my ability. We did not break any rules and Bruce acted entirely within his rights.

When the interview began, the officers seemed to have completely forgotten about the forensic evidence and the evidence from the autopsy and proceeded with the interview as though their lives depended upon it.

I had to interrupt on no less than three occasions when I thought that they were over-stepping the bounds and I knew that I was running a substantial risk of being asked to leave the interview.

It finally became clear to the police that the interview had begun to move in circles as there was no new ground for them. However, Bruce did admit that there had been an incident and an exchange of words which the police thought sufficient to charge Bruce with being in breach of the peace. This placed him in breach of his bind-over from the earlier occasion, so giving the police something for all their efforts.

He was to be placed before the court the following morning, which put me in severe difficulties. I thought he should have been bailed but the police had other ideas. As well as having cases in Rotherham I had a case in Barnsley for an old client and I had promised to turn up.

I toyed with the idea of doing Pontefract first and then back to Rotherham and then flying across the Barnsley, but it was a forlorn hope with little prospect of me being able to succeed with it.

I decided that I would have to instruct an agent in Barnsley and deal with the Pontefract matter first and then travel to Rotherham. It was asking for trouble, and indeed I got it. Thankfully my old mate Peter Hollingworth dug me out of the proverbial in Barnsley.

When I arrived at Pontefract there was a queue to get on and for one reason or another they all needed to get on first. Even the old pals act could not assure me of the first place in the queue.

The court clerk was particularly unhelpful and had got out of the wrong side of the bed that morning and the prosecutor was one who seemed to make a point of not reading my files.

I managed to get back to Rotherham by 12 noon having secured conditional bail for Bruce, albeit on relatively minor charges. I had hoped to deal with the case there and then, to avoid the necessity of having to travel back to Pontefract, but despite the fact that Bruce's luck was in, mine was out and a month later I had to once again sample the delights of the pie shop opposite the court.

On my return to the Rotherham court I was greeted by the emphasemic usher who, despite a dreadful cough, was smoking his beloved Capstan full-strength. His greeting was interspersed with a chesty cough.

"You're in for it this morning Steve, the court's been retired for twenty minutes waiting for you."

"Haven't they got any other work to do?" I asked.

"No, the trial finished early and they split the work up with the result that everyone was finished by about half past eleven."

"Bloody marvellous," I said to myself.

I would not have minded the grade four bollocking had it not been for the fact that I was just trying to do a days work. I was not skiving or enjoying myself, but was just making my own life a misery to suit everyone else. I put on my tin hat and armour plated vest and went to face the music.

The magistrates were quite sympathetic, despite the fact that they had been kept waiting and I was grateful to them for that. The clients were not as sympathetic.

"I suppose tha stopped in bed this morning?" said one of the wingers.

"Yes I have," I said. "I was drunk last night and decided I'd stop in bed and I feel much better for it thank you."

The speed of my repartee left him for dead and as I went to deal with a more sympathetic client, I could discern the words 'idle bastard' as I walked down the litter-strewn corridor.

My list finished just before 1pm and when I got back to the office there was a telephone call from Bruce Johnson.

I thought that it was particularly nice that he should ring me to give me a vote of thanks for my efforts, but I was to be disappointed.

"Is that you Steve?" said Bruce.

"Yes, it is. How are you now?" I asked.

"Better for being out of that bloody hole," said Bruce. "I'll tell you why I'm ringing.."

"Yes," I said, expecting Bruce Johnson's Award for Industry.

"I want to know when I can have my trainers back, the police have kept them."

Perhaps he was going to give me the vote of thanks at the end, but I was to be disappointed.

"You'll have to wait until you see what happens about the charges, Bruce. If they take no action then of course you are entitled to them back. If they continue with the proceedings then I feel sure you should get them at the end of the case."

"Do you think I'm going to get done then?" said Bruce, "For this breach of the peace lark?"

"Well," I said, "Who can tell. The police have got to have something on their books, after all a chap has died."

"Ah, but that wasn't my fault, he was dying anyway. I just wish he hadn't poisoned me dog.

"Yes, well I can understand why that would get up your nose, but I think he's paid the ultimate penalty don't you?"

"It was still my dog," said Bruce.

"Yes, I know it was," I said, giving him one final opportunity to redeem himself and show me that he was not like most of the rest.

"Reight," said Bruce, "I will let thee know if I'm done or not." With that all I could hear was the dialling tone.

"Thank you very much indeed Mr Smith for your sterling work and effort, on inconveniencing yourself so greatly over the past two or three days, running round at my beck and call, missing meals, creating ulcers and receiving bollockings from magistrates." I said to myself.

Just then Tracey had entered to catch the end of my protestations.

"Are you talking to yourself Mr Smith?"

"Yes," I said, "I'm just being very grateful on someone's behalf."

"Oh, that's very nice of you," said Tracey.

She picked up the file she was looking for and disappeared.

I turned to look out of the window which overlooked the churchyard.

I remembered the words my old boss Bill Harthill once told me,

"If you expect thanks in this game, you will be disappointed, and if its thanks that you're after, join the Salvation Army."

As I wandered upstairs to the filing room I couldn't help wondering if you were allowed to drink in the Salvation Army.

Just before the next hearing of Bruce's case, the charge against him was dropped. I wrote to him with the good news and pointing out that he could collect his trainers from the Pontefract police station.

I did not receive a reply.

Chapter Eleven

THE SINS OF THE FATHER

I had first met Gaynor Pearson in 1982. Now just over a year later she was back in my office accompanying her mother, Marie who had an appointment with me to discuss what steps she could take to force her common-law husband Kevin out of the 'matrimonial' home.

Marie Pearson had become an unmarried mother in 1964 when she was just sixteen. She had known the father of her child for only two weeks when Gaynor was conceived. She loved him because he looked like Paul McCartney, the good looking one in the new pop group, The Beatles. The relationship didn't last as long as "She Loves You" was in the Top Ten. By Bonfire Night he had left the area and by Christmas Marie had missed her second period.

When Gaynor was born Marie lived with her parents until she got fed up with them trying to run her life. She found a bed-sit and left Gaynor with child-minders while she went out to work. By the time Gaynor started school Marie had met Kevin, an unemployed labourer who, after a few weeks, had suggested that they set up home together. They moved into a council house and had the rent book in joint names. This was to be the only real commitment Kevin was to make to the relationship. He soon showed Marie that he was a bully and a drunkard who would happily take out his dissatisfaction with life on his partner and her child. By the time Gaynor was six she had learnt that when her stepfather came home drunk, she had to hide in her bedroom well out of the way so that she could not be the focal point of yet another argument. Nevertheless there were many times when she would lie on

204

her bed in tears with her pillow over her ears trying to block out the sounds of her mother being beaten.

On a 'dole day' evening in August last year she had been subjected to yet another beating. It was no different from the countless other times Kevin had hit her but finally she snapped. She took the poker from the fireplace and struck back, hitting him so hard that he was knocked unconscious, sustaining serious head injuries including a hairline fracture of the skull. He bled profusely until the arrival of the emergency services who managed to give him emergency treatment to save his life.

As Kevin was being treated in Rotherham Hospital Marie was interviewed by the police and who afforded her every courtesy and, if I dare say it, assistance during the taking of contemporaneous notes, so that her case could be placed in the best possible light.

She was bailed immediately the interview was over and allowed to go home to her children, having been charged with grievous bodily harm.

Gaynor had brought her to see me after they had been informed that she was to appear before the magistrates court the following week. From her statement I got the impression that the police felt they had had to spend considerable resources in dealing with this bully over the years, and I suspected they believed Marie had given him nothing less than he deserved.

Sometimes it is unfortunate that the law is not able to look at things in this way but the courts' attitude has always been that violence cannot be condoned in any form whatsoever.

On that particular occasion, I did not agree with the proposition and I advised Marie to plead not guilty despite the serious nature of the assault, on the grounds of self defence.

However, Marie pleaded guilty and was placed on probation for three years which was probably the best course.

Now a year later Gaynor was back in my office with her mother and she watched intently as Marie told me of her problems. She had finally decided that it was time to take steps to have the bully thrown out of her home. Kevin was not prepared to go and had made many pitiful promises to mend his ways, but unfortunately when in drink his promises were always broken.

Marie was clearly a woman who had suffered a great deal, enduring a life of violence and unhappiness. Apart from the physical signs which included a badly damaged top lip which had obviously needed some surgery, the years of abuse had dulled her personality, destroyed whatever confidence she had ever had and had even made her think that she might be to blame for Kevin's behaviour.

Marie assured me that there had been good times that there were the twins to think about. She said that his conduct towards them had not been nearly as bad. At this point Gaynor interrupted, tutting quite fiercely and shaking her head.

"No Gaynor, he's been alright with them," said Marie.

"I don't think so mother," said Gaynor sitting back in her chair in an attempt to conceal her anger. Her face could not disguise the hatred she had for her stepfather.

"Have you got on with him at all Gaynor?" I asked pointedly.

"Not at all," she said, "He is a drunk and an offensive pig and as a man he is a coward. My mother has had to put up with his nasty behaviour, his beatings, all his meanness, and worst of all he has taken away her identity."

It was quite clear just how much she hated him, and even more apparent that her mother could not find it in herself to argue. It was a grim acceptance of an endless catalogue of shame.

"What about your mouth?" said Gaynor, "How can you excuse that?" she demanded.

Maria lifted her hand in a forlorn attempt to conceal her top lip, making the disfigurement even more apparent.

"What are we going to do about it?" I asked, trying to direct the conversation away from Marie's humiliation.

"Can you help us?" she asked. "Can we do it in such a way that I do not have to be in the house, because if he knows we have been here we will be for it."

"We will have to issue proceedings and they will have to be served upon him," I said. "Have you anywhere else to stay until we get the matter before the court?"

"I could stay with my sister," said Marie, "But she would only be able to put me up, because there is no room for the others. Where would Gaynor and the boys go?"

"Don't worry about me," snapped Gaynor. "I've told you before, I will be alright and we will find somewhere for the boys."

"How old are they?" I asked.

"Fourteen," said Gaynor. The twins had been born within a year of Marie and Kevin setting up house together, but if Marie had thought that having his own children would have changed Kevin, she was wrong.

"How do they get on with their father?" I queried.

"Very well really," said Marie brightening up.

"No they don't," said Gaynor. "They are frightened of him and well you know it."

Marie gave no answer. If ever there was a time I felt sorry for a fellow human being it was then.

"I will complete all the necessary papers and then I will need to see you in a day or so in order to take a full statement, which can be filed with the case papers.   Will you come and see me on Friday at about this time?"

"Of course she will," said Gaynor, answering for her mother. "I'll see to it that she is here," and with that they both left.

Marie walked with a slight stoop and wore a coat that had clearly seen better days.   Her shoes were down at the heel and her hair was entering the final phase of the life span of her last perm.   She was the typical down trodden and abused woman. However, there was an air of defiance about her daughter that made it quite clear that she was not going to follow in her mother's footsteps.

Later that evening I prepared the papers for the case by looking at some old precedents.   Only the names had to be changed.   Unfortunately such cases are all too common.

The next day I was to file the papers at court and all I needed was Marie's signature.

Gaynor arrived on time but Marie was not with her.

"Where is she?" I asked.

"I thought she would be here.   I've not come from home…..she said she would he here……where is she?"

After a while we both realised she was not coming.   I really felt for Gaynor and for a moment I was unsure of what to say.

"Perhaps she's been delayed…….missed her bus even……..a number of things………"

My excuses fell on stoney ground.   Gaynor remained silent; I suppose she could not think of anything to say.

Finally, I said, "I'll keep the papers handy and when she's ready I'll see to it."   I tried to be as positive as I could but I knew how Gaynor felt.

She did not say a word, but just looked at me with half a smile on her face;   it was a face of resignation.   She was embarrassed and could find nothing else to say except to thank me for my help, after which she left.   The following day I was walking through the town centre when I noticed a couple walking towards me. The woman was familiar, although a black eye and swollen mouth disguised the face somewhat. Our eyes met for a second but Marie looked away pretending not to have seen me. The man was oblivious to both of us as he walked at quite a pace, with the woman attempting to keep up by the odd hastily taken few steps when she fell behind.

I saw Gaynor again about a week later. She had finally left home and rented a one roomed flat just out of town. She had no intention of returning home even for a visit, but still expressed concern about her mother.

As soon as I left the office the following Friday, I dismissed any thoughts of work as that weekend was to be our last trip of the year to the Lake District. Since discovering the beauty of the area a few years earlier, I had formed an attachment to the place, particularly Bowness on Windermere, and when work permitted Wilf and I would take our wives for weekends away from it all.

Initially, much of our time was taken up sightseeing and seeking out the best hotels, restaurants and occasionally the odd public house. However on our last few visits we had found ourselves looking at 'for sale' boards in front of properties set in some of the most wonderful surroundings in the world and imagining ourselves as the owners. We had even stopped to look in estate agents windows on our way to our favourite pubs. This must have been serious but we had taken it no further until that weekend.

Wilf couldn't make that particular trip and so Jennifer and I invited Christopher Good and his wife Pat to join us.

Goody and I had been friends from being three years old. We had met at the local nursery school when I lived in South Kirkby. My father was employed by the Co-op as a butcher and Chris's parents were the licensees of the local Working Mens' Club. I remember as a youngster visiting the club and sitting with the old men in the smoke room, listening to their stories of humour and tragedy from the local mines where they had spent the whole of their working lives.

On the Saturday afternoon, Goody and I went for a stroll via a couple of pubs in the town before reaching Hayton and Winkley, a local estate agent in Bowness.

There were a large number of properties advertised in the window including No 4 Priory Cottages, Windermere. For some reason it caught my eye and before I realised it I had dragged Goody back to the hotel car park to get the car and we were on our way to view a desirable lakeland property. We finally found it, well hidden from the road behind a hotel called the Priory, which had been built in the shape of a mediaeval priory by a local eccentric some years before.

As we drove down a tarmac track to the rear of the hotel we saw two rows of cottages, one further up the slope than the other to allow both to have a most splendid view of the lake. In front of the cottages was a large open lawn, leading to a car park with two spaces for each cottage. It looked perfect.

The car park was almost empty so we parked and after a quick look at the outside of No 4 we took a small winding cinder track which led through two adjoining fields to the water's edge and a large mooring of recent construction which stuck out onto the lake. The mooring was approximately one third of the way down the lake from Windermere itself, towards Ambleside. I was totally and completely captivated. My mind was made up in an instant and we drove back to the estate agents for more information, the keys and a conducted viewing. We got all three and by the time Goody and I returned to our wives at the hotel, I was hooked.

The cottage was certainly in need of repairs and re-decoration. It was cold and rather damp, and it was clear that at sometime in the recent past the plumbing had suffered a burst. The front door opened into a relatively small lounge and kitchenette area, which in turn led to a very small hall off which was a bathroom and shower and two small bedrooms, one of which was only big enough for bunk beds or a single. It was very small, but quaint, and I believed the potential was fantastic.

That night we dined in the Old England Hotel. It was a lovely old hotel in the centre of town, and although it had been bought by one of the large hotel chains it had tried to retain its 'Olde worlde atmosphere'. The dining room overlooked the lake which was beyond a small lawned area which had a swimming pool inset into it.

Goody and I sat on the terrace overlooking the lake and I talked endlessly about the potential of the cottage. He realised that I had been smitten and I believed that there was absolutely no doubt that the cottage had to be mine.

On the Monday I returned to work and told Wilf of my exploits, and he agreed to go with me the following weekend to see 'our cottage'.

After the visit Wilf agreed completely and the first thing we did on the Monday was to see our friend and accountant Michael Jarvis with a view to discussing how we could acquire the property.

Within a few days we put in an offer which was accepted by return and within four weeks Wilf had completed the sale. We had become property owners in the Lake District. It was yet another financial commitment, but somehow it did not seem to matter as I felt that no sacrifice was too great for this particular venture.

Although it was only a few weeks before Christmas, our weekends became devoted to cleaning the place up and even my parents were co-opted to help with the painting and decorating. I was determined that the cottage would be ready for the following Easter and nothing would stand in our way.

On the first Monday in December, I had a large court list beckoning. At that time I had no-one else with whom to share the court work, and I was finding it increasingly more difficult to satisfy our ever-growing number of clients.

I surveyed the court diary for the list that morning and rang the cells to see if there were any prisoners of whom I was unaware.

I was told that I had three new prisoners, but the names had not been put on the board and all they could tell me was that they were male.

I turned up early so as to try to be ready with the prisoners for a 10.00am start and steal a march upon my other colleagues in the list.

I saw Cyril Jackson first, a local neer-do-well who had all the makings of becoming a good, loyal and very regular client.

Unfortunately, there was little I could do for him because he had a lot of charges to face and decided, quite sensibly, that there was no point in adjourning his case. He knew that he was going to prison and felt that the sooner he got there the sooner he would get out.

The chairman of the magistrates was a tweed suited spinster of some considerable experience, but she was short on sympathy and it was obvious from the outset where Cyril was going.

"Cyril Jackson, you will go to prison for three months," said the tweed suited lady magistrate, "Take him down please."

"You old cow," shouted the disappointed defendant.

212

"What did your client say?" asked the magistrate, peering over her horn rimmed glasses.

I had to think very quickly to avoid being placed in a very embarrassing situation.

"I think he was expressing some considerable regret at his sentence   Madam."

The magistrate turned first to her colleague on her left, as if to ask for confirmation of what had been said, and then to one on her right.

Whether they had heard what the defendant said, I am unable to say, but it appeared that Cyril's words were not repeated and my plight was relieved by the magistrates clerk calling on the next case.

Cyril had been sentenced for two charges of burglary and a number of TIC's. He had a long list of previous convictions and had failed to comply with a community service order which had required him to do unpaid work for the community as penance for his sins. It seemed to me that the magistrates had little option but to dispatch him into the arms of Her Majesty's Jailers, but he had disagreed with the decision, and of course he would be right because he was the defendant.

I was reflecting upon my contribution to the ever increasing prison community when the emphasemic usher tapped me on the shoulder, coughed in an attempt to spread his germs along the solicitor's bench, and told me that two unnamed clients wanted to speak with me immediately.

It is annoying when this happens because having fought to get into the queue to get your cases called as soon as possible, to be dragged out of the same queue for something inconsequential, such as to see if you have a light, a packet of cigarettes or some bus fare to get home, means you lose your place.

I turned to the usher. "I've only just got to the front of the queue. What the bloody hell does he want?" I asked.

The emphasemic usher did not know what they wanted and indeed I shouldn't really have expected him to, for he was doing me a favour by passing on the message. Pausing to cough into my ear again the usher said, "They say it's very urgent and it could be a matter of life and death."

"It could be a matter of life and death for them if I lose my place," I said in annoyance. "Tell them I'll be along shortly. If they go and get a cup of tea I will join them in the tea room as soon as possible."

The usher was kind enough to pass on the message, but it was only a matter of a moment or so before he returned. I knew it was him because I felt the force of his cough in my ear.

"Mr Smith," said the usher.

"Yes," I replied politely, but really wanting to stick my biro up his nose.

"They ask if you have any change for the tea?"

With a groan I reached into my pocket and brought out a pound coin which I handed to the usher, who walked off smiling and coughing.

My visitors were none other than Jack and Albert who, in their own way, represented a considerable part of my income. They were, without doubt, the most loyal clients I had.

I was just wondering what problem Jack had brought me this time when.......

"Which case next Mr Smith?" said the clerk to the justices. "Excuse me, that's the second time I've asked you."

"I beg your pardon," I replied concentrating on the matter in hand.

"Are you Michael Wellington McIver of 2 Lansdown Crescent Eastwood Rotherham?" asked the clerk.

"Yes Miss," said my client Spider.

"Yes Miss?" I asked myself. "Spider must be having trouble with his eyesight."

I looked left and saw Michael Wellington McIver, also known as Spider, the boy with the tattoos all over his face. The lady magistrate peered over the top of her horn rimmed glasses and stared at this unwelcome guest with some displeasure. She could not help but ask,

"Are those tattoos all over that young man's face Mr Smith?"

"I'm afraid so madam," I replied.

"Did he know what he was doing?" asked the magistrate.

"I often wonder Madam, although he tells me that the tattoo on the forehead saying Ford Cortina Mark 4 was actually put there by one of his friends while he was drunk."

I heard the lady magistrate turn to one of her colleagues, and the words 'disgraceful sight' were just about audible. At least I think she said 'sight', though I could have been mistaken. Then again either word would have been appropriate.

Spider had been caught in possession of amphetamine sulphate, a drug popularly known as speed. He was in rather a poor state but I had to admit he had been in a poor state before drugs. However his condition had worsened as the addiction gripped him, leaving his face grey and drawn as he sniffed repeatedly as though he had a cold, a tell tale sign of amphetamine abuse. He had just been released from serving a two year prison sentence for possession with intent to supply and within a month he was at it again.

The charge this time was simple possession, but he was still in a serious position and the court would be looking for a return to custody.

Spider was pleading guilty and then his case would be adjourned to enable probation reports to be prepared so that we could try and get the Probation Service to come up with some suggestion as to how to deal with him which might avoid the necessity of another 'free holiday' with the prison service.

My application for reports was granted immediately and the magistrates made it quite clear that they took a serious view of the case and were considering imprisonment.

"Not again," said Spider, "I've only just come out."

I leaned across to him and whispered,

"Just be quiet for the moment Spider, otherwise you'll only just be going in again."

We were given a date to return to court to be sentenced and Spider was given his bail form.   I told him to wait in the corridor until I completed my next case, which I did as quickly as possible and left the relatively clear atmosphere of the court room to enter the putrescent public corridor which was a veritable rogues gallery of peering eyes watching every move of the court users comings and goings.

Jack and Albert were sitting quietly in the WRVS tea room and when I entered they both stood to attention as if some urgent matters required my devoted consideration.

"What's up Jack?" I asked.

Before he could answer we were interrupted by a motley looking fellow with long, black, exceptionally greasy hair and a mouth full of black teeth, framed by cracked and sore lips. He seemed to have formed a close affinity to his suit, which I am sure he had not taken off in a long time.   His face had seen neither soap and water nor the threat of a razor blade for many days.   His eyes were dark and bloodshot and he looked eagerly from side to side as if expecting a visit from a debt collector at any moment.   He spoke with a Scottish accent in a rather low and secretive tone, punctuated by regular helpings of the 'f' word as if to add that extra emphasis to certain areas of his conversation.

"I've a fucking charge; deception O.K. It's a wee problem. It's a straight forward not guilty plea. There's no evidence, so they'll have to let me off and if they don't I'll appeal anyway. I want to adjourn it today because I'm going back home to Scotland for three months, and I want it adjourning until I come back. There shouldn't be any problem with that should there?" His question sounded more like a statement.

"Oh it's as simple as that is it!" I replied sarcastically.

"Aye," came the reply, "It certainly is."

With that the emphasemic usher approached me and said, "They're calling one of your cases on in court two Steve."

"I'll be back in two minutes Jack, I've just got to see what court two want."

"What about me?" Our Scots friend interrupted.

"I'll see you in two minutes. Just let me sort this out," I said, and with that the jailer appeared and told me they had brought in another prisoner who had to go to hospital and he needed to see me straightaway.

I agreed, but as I was running to court two I felt someone tugging at the back of my coat.

"Lend's a quid for a cup of tea Steve," said my assailant.

"I'm, sorry pal, I don't have any change," I replied, which found no favour, though for once it was true.

"That's what they all say," he said sulkily.

With that I was told that there was someone wanting to speak with me on the telephone in the cell area.

I stood quietly and counted to ten to avoid the oncoming pulmonary embolism.

I was back on track and about to enter court two when the hem on my jacket which thankfully I had had the foresight to reinforce, was yanked. Turning I was confronted with another unfamiliar face and a torrent of garbled words and spluttered crumbs from a bun he was trying to eat. He was so

217

determined to speak that he had forgotten that his mouth was full of baking and attempted to share it with me as he spoke.

"The coppers have done me, reight, and I aint' done it, reight, and I'm not having it, reight. So it's a not guilty plea, reight, and whether they like it or not, reight, I'm not having it. I've been dragged here on this spoonest charge."

"Do you mean spurious?" I asked.

"Yes, spoonest charge, and I'm not having it, reight."

He thrust a set of summonses into my hand, which had clearly been used as a plate mat in a Chinese Restaurant. Parts of the set were still wet, and I couldn't imagine where he had been keeping those.

I noticed that the charges related to no television licence, for which he would not be able to get legal aid, and yet he was berating me as though I had issued the summons against him myself.

I kept my composure, however, and refrained from kneeing him in the groin. I handed him his summonses back using the tip of my thumb and forefinger and said that I would speak with him as soon as I could.

He continued to shout his disquiet into the space behind me as I entered the solemnity which was court number two. The magistrates were reading a probation report but looked up on hearing the commotion to see who the infiltrator was. I got the distinct impression that they were blaming me for the noise, despite the fact that I had absolutely nothing to do with it.

The usher intervened and escorted the young man back into the reception area with the word 'reight' ringing through the court corridor as he went.

I finally dealt with my case in court number two, took a deep breath and re-entered the cauldron which was the court corridor.

I dodged the areas of spillage of the WRVS coffee, and the feet of one of the town drunks who was strung across the corridor singing a slightly off-key version of 'Eaelweiss'. I returned to the 'rat hole' interview room at the end of the corridor, where I was joined by Jack and Albert.

"Tha looks 'arassed Steve," said Jack.

If you ever admit to being 'arassed' you can give the impression that you are too busy, which can put clients off and so I chose my words carefully.

"Not really Jack," I said, "It's nothing we can't handle, is it Albert?" I said with a smile, attempting to draw the young man into the conversation.

"Tha what?" said Albert, who clearly missed what I had said.

"What's to do then Jack?" I asked.

"Coppers have got our Morris and they are going to interview him. Tha knows what Morris is like, he'll admit to owt when his knackers are squeezed."

"I don't think the CID will be doing that to him," I said seriously.

"Tha knows what I mean," said Jack, "It's an expression like."

"I understand," I replied smiling, "I'll finish my list and get down to the police station straight away."

"Can tha ring 'em, said Jack. "I don't want him interviewing before tha's there."

I reassured him and they both left, and as they did so the man with the mouthful of cake was at me again.

"What about this, or what then like?" he said.

"Get yourself another bun and I will be with you in a minute," I said as I raced into court one to regain my place.

The rest of the morning went reasonably well, although Cyril was rather upset about his sentence.

The man with the cake went away satisfied after we arrived at a suitable and proper arrangement with the prosecutor, and the

Scotsman was nowhere to be found. I suspected he had adjourned his own case.

When I got to the police station, the custody sergeant confirmed that they were not squeezing Morris's knackers, but he had released him with no charge. I telephoned Jack straight away, who thanked me enthusiastically saying that I was the 'best thing since sliced bread.'

I told him that I had done nothing but Jack's reply said it all.

"Ah, but tha were there, weren't tha. Tha turned up and he got out."

"Yes Jack, but I didn't actually do anything."

"Get away, tha must have done. E's out int 'e. Anyway, thanks Steve, I'll buy thee a bottle of whisky for the trouble."

"There's no need Jack, I'm happy to oblige," and with that I rang off.

The conversation with Jack represented one of the many peculiarities of this profession. If the defendant gets an extremely good result, whether it's through your skills or not, you get the credit and the slaps on the back. However, when a defendant gets what he believes is a bad result usually because he has offended and deserves it, the solicitor often gets the blame. I have heard many defendants saying things like "I don't like him, he got me three years," when referring to solicitors and barristers.

I got back to the office just before 2.00pm to find a man pacing up and down the reception area.

"Thank God you're here," he said. "You've got to go the general hospital to see Marie Pearson. He's beaten her up good and proper this time. Gaynor's with her now. If you get a minute can you go up and see them?"

"What's happened?" I asked as the messenger set off down the stairs.

"They'll tell you at the hospital," he said, and disappeared out of the door.

I was confronted by yet another client with a large wad of summonses in his hand. He looked at me and grinned. I managed a smile but then side-stepped him, went into my office and picked up the telephone. I got through to the hospital straightaway and discovered that Marie was in the casualty ward.

It seemed that she had been the subject of a violent attack which had left her with multiple cuts and bruises to her face and body, but more seriously, she had sustained a depressed fracture of her right cheek and had lost three of her front teeth.

I arranged to visit her at tea-time and then set about dealing with my many appointments. I had a mixed bag that afternoon including two divorces, one no T.V. licence, two burglars and a relic from the Hippy era of the late sixties who had been "done for smoking happy fags man."

At the end of the day declined the kind offer to join Wilf, who was entertaining three of the local insurance brokers, Pagey, Andrew Lovell and Dave Eastwood, for a drink and a game on the space invader.

I arrived at the hospital at 6.00pm and was shown to a small room off one of the wards. Gaynor, was sitting on a chair beside the bed holding her mother's hand. I was shocked to see Marie in such a dreadful condition. Both her eyes were badly swollen and had started to bruise. Her right cheek was clearly depressed and her lips were stitched and swollen. There were scratches all over her face and neck and I could see thumb prints around the area of her throat.

She was clearly in a great deal of discomfort, and as she attempted to speak she began to cry.

"Don't mother," said a tearful Gaynor, "It will be alright."

I did not need to be told how she had come by her injuries, and certainly not who had inflicted them, but I was interested to know if the police had been involved.

"No," snapped Gaynor, "The police have not been told, so he has got away with it yet again. The police arrived at the same time as the ambulance but she refused to make a complaint."

Marie became even more upset, forcing Gaynor to stop talking about what had happened. The poor girl only had her mother's welfare at heart.

"One day," said Gaynor, "One day," her voice tailed off as she remembered our conversation.

Marie did her best to speak, but as she was clearly in pain, I did my very best to ask as few questions as possible.

Gaynor chipped in with other details. It seemed that Kevin had come home drunk and found that some money which he had put on the sideboard for cigarettes had been spent on bread. He accused Marie of stealing it and when she explained what she had used it for, he lost his temper and started to hit her repeatedly about the face. When she could take no more, she fell to the floor, where he kicked her in the stomach and then grabbed her around the throat. It was only when she went limp in his hands that he realised he had gone too far. Fortunately for Marie she had just blacked out momentarily, but had the assault continued it could well have been a mortuary rather than a hospital that she was taken to.

"My mother wishes to take this matter to court Mr Smith, and this time she will turn up. Isn't that right mother?" Gaynor looked at Marie, who nodded in grim acceptance. She knew that she really had no alternative.

I could just make out the words "He nearly killed me" before I asked her to rest while I completed my notes.

"What's more," said Gaynor, "We want him out of the house."

I nodded thoughtfully as I wondered about Marie's future. Surely no woman would be prepared to put up with this level of abuse.

It was a week before Marie could leave the hospital, during which time I had prepared all the documents and had them served. From the day she had been taken into hospital, Kevin had made no attempt to see her or even find out how she was getting on. Surely in those circumstances Marie would go through with the case.

As the hearing was only four days away I invited Marie to the office to ensure that she would not change her mind.

That evening we were to play a football match against a firm of solicitors from Sheffield. They were captained by my old friend Brian Jones who at that time was a legal executive with a Sheffield firm. Brian was balding and putting on weight, but he could still play a good game of football despite his advancing years. The match was a sporting one and ended with the scores level at seven each. We all met in the bar afterwards and arranged a rematch, but the drink could not dull the pain in my foot. Unfortunately, during the match I had injured my big toe, aggravating my ongoing in-growing toe nail problem. By the time I got to work the following day I was limping quite badly and despite the cries of 'gout' from my colleagues, I managed to go about my daily work as usual. Marie kept her appointment and, while she looked much better than when I had seen her in hospital, she was still adamant that she was going through with the court action.

I then headed for Rotherham court where Spider was back for sentencing. It was the luck of the draw as to which magistrate would deal with the case and it turned out to be the very same Magistrate who had adjourned his case for reports four weeks before.

At the original hearing she had been far from impressed by either Spider's personality or demeanour, not to mention the tattoos of various spiders in their webs crawling all over his face and the words 'Ford Cortina Mark 4' across his forehead. But then, who could blame her?

On the other hand, the probation officer had, as always, a great deal of sympathy for poor old Spider and I felt he got it absolutely right when he said that Mr McKeiver had been a victim of circumstance and misfortune. He had also been the victim of those much more devious than he in his attempt to gain acceptance among those who pretended to be his friends.

Spider had been the brunt of everyone's jokes and callous remarks, which I suspect contributed to the reasons why he took up drugs. He had then become the unwitting tool of villains, and one in particular who was significant by his absence from court that day.

I had seen Spider in the rat hole interview room and had gone through the report with him very carefully. It recommended that he be placed in a probation hostel well away from the area for a period of twelve months, to live there and abide by their rules and regulations. This seemed highly appropriate in Spider's case, because just about everything else had been tried, including prison which had achieved absolutely nothing except a further burden upon the tax payer's purse. I realise that in some cases there is no option but to impose imprisonment as it is necessary for the protection of the public, but in the case of someone like Spider it does not achieve an awful lot other than simply putting the problem away until the next time.

I attempted to persuade the court that one last chance would be appropriate in Spider's case.

As we left the rat hole interview room I found Jack waiting for me in the corridor.

"What's to do Jack?" I asked.

"Aye-up Steve," said Jack, "Have you got a minute, I need to ask your advice about something."

"Certainly," I said and invited him into the rat hole.

"Steve?" said Jack earnestly.

"Yes Jack," I replied, equally as earnestly.

"What would you do if you were me?" Before Jack finished his question I pondered exactly what I would do if I were him. I thought of all sorts of things like killing his son Albert and turning to religion, but before I could contemplate the matter further Jack came to the point.

"You see it's like this Steve; I've got the chance of a job."

"You've what?" I said looking at the man incredulously. He was fifty years old and had never worked for anyone in his life.

"A job? Do you mean as in working for a living?"

"Aye," said Jack, "Tha sees me and Madge have been thinking about things and we thought that it might be a good idea like."

"Bloody hell Jack," I said, "Steady on. It's a bit extreme isn't it?"

"Well it's a good job tha sees, and it's what I like doing," said Jack slightly embarrassed.

"What is it?" I asked.

"There's this bloke tha sees, he's reight wealthy, and his passion is pigeons. Well he's fancied my Arse for ages and he offered me four grand for him. That's a lot of money for my Arse."

"That's a lot of money for anyone's arse," I thought to myself.

"He's a millionaire tha knows, anyway I've sold Arse to him and he's asked me to look after his racing stables."

I couldn't believe that the pigeon world had their own millionaire backed racing stables, but clearly they did.

"He says he would gimme a good wage an we can live on his farm in caravans. We went last week to 'ave a look. It's reight nice, 'int kids think it's great, that's all except our Albert."

"What's Albert's problem?" I asked.

"Well it's a long way from his mates tha sees, and he dunt want to move."

"Where is it Jack?" I asked.

"Geordie land, up in Northumberland," said Jack, "On a farm neart coast. He's wanting to breed pigeons and he's going to put my Arse to stud."

"When will you have to go?" I asked resisting the temptation to smile.

Jack paused for a little as if in reflection.

"End of the year," said Jack

"This year?" I asked.

"Aye," said Jack, "It's a bit sudden like, but he wants to get on wi' it and get started. He's asked me to move up by Christmas. These millionaires are a bit pushy tha knows."

"But you'll have to give up your council house," I suggested.

"Aye", said Jack, "That's the problem. But I'm fed up of this area. I'm getting too old to keep getting into trouble, and it'll be a nice new start for Madge 'int kids"

"But what about Albert?" I asked.

"Well, our family's always stuck together through thick and thin. I know that people sometimes laugh at us 'cos we aint got much, but we are reight as a family. If we fall out it's soon o'er wi' and sorted, and anyway I've never 'ɔd a job."

At that moment I looked at him and saw the face of a man who had lived a fairly uncomplicated life bringing up nine children in near poverty and adversity. Many people would say he was nothing more than a common criminal, and I suppose they would be right, but in his own way he had a

226

sense of honour and a strong moral code. He never compromised me and he was always a delight to act for, and I'm not ashamed to say that I liked him. He sat before me on the brink of a momentous decision. He was a charming man in many ways, but a bit of a bugger with other people's property, particularly the 'commercials'. As I listened to him describe his new found job I could see excitement and pride appear on his face. This was to be his first job at fifty and he would be doing something he was actually good at. Perhaps it would be the making of him.

"Well we'll certainly miss you and the kids Jack and even that little bugger Albert," I said smiling.

Jack just laughed his singular laugh and shrugged his shoulders before taking a deep breath as he posed the question.

"Does tha think I'm doing reight?" said Jack. Tha sees it's a big risk giving up our homes an' all, but I just feel that I've got to 'ave a go."

"If you really want to do it Jack, and if you think it will work out, have a go. If you don't you will always regret it and will always wonder whether or not it would have worked out. Of course it's a risk, but sometimes in life you've no option but to take them. Sometimes it turns out well and sometimes you have egg on your face. Unfortunately, this is one question that only you and the family can answer. I wouldn't like to point you in any direction but I just hope you won't have any regrets either way."

"I see what you mean," said Jack. "I might always wonder what it might 've been like and I might kick me sen if I don't try."

Jack then stood to leave, but before doing so held out his hand, which I took firmly.

227

"Thanks for everything," said Jack. "I hope we'll see you before we go. Tha can come down for thee dinner wun neet."

The following day was matrimonial day at court and all the parties were sat in the corridor outside court number three, with the men on one side and the women on the other.

I looked through the list in the solicitors room and I found Marie Pearson near the bottom.

She had brought an action for a personal protection order against her common-law husband. The names of the solicitors were on the list, and I noticed that our name was spelt wrongly, 'Wilfred Smith'. I laughed and Marie smiled a half smile as we entered court. Kevin had not attended and the application went through on the nod.

As soon as I got back to the office I saw Wilf and told him about Jack and his family.

"Does that mean that little shit Albert won't be coming and bothering us again?"

"Yes, I suppose it does," I said.

Wilf just sneered and left me to reflect upon the loss of our best clients.

Exactly one week later I was driving to work listening to Radio Sheffield when I heard a report that a woman was to appear in court charged with attempted murder. I was shocked when I heard that the woman was none other than Marie Pearson. When I arrived at Rotherham court later that morning I found that Marie had seen another solicitor, but Gaynor was waiting and very anxious to see me.

"I need to speak to you Mr Smith," said Gaynor.

"Of course, you can come with me," I said and took her to the rat hole interview room. Gaynor was trembling and beside herself with worry.

"It's my mother. I think she's admitted trying to kill him," she blurted out.

"Just wait a moment," I said, "Try and calm down and tell me exactly what's happened."

"You see it was all about me, this is all my fault. There was an argument at home and it resulted in my mum losing her temper. But it was all my fault." Gaynor started to cry.

"Look, wait a minute. I'll get you some tea. Just wait there."

I went to the WRVS canteen and collected two pots of coffee-coloured tea, but by the time I got back to the rat hole Gaynor had gone.

However, a little later in the morning I saw Marie being brought into court, handcuffed to two burly female officers.

Although it wasn't my case, I stood at the back of the court by the door and listened intently as the prosecutor made his application for a remand in custody.

His opening told the story that on the night in question Kevin came home drunk earlier than usual. Marie was there with Gaynor, who had been making one of her rare visits.

When Kevin found Gaynor in the house, he lost his temper and there was an argument. He struck Gaynor, and also Marie, when she tried to interfere. He then put his hands around Gaynor's throat, and Marie picked up a pair of scissors and stabbed him repeatedly. Marie then telephoned the emergency services and an ambulance came, followed by the Rotherham Police.

There could be no doubt that this was a very serious allegation, and the prosecutor read out the fact that the complainant was fighting for life in Rotherham District General Hospital.

His condition had been aggravated by the fact that he was drunk and the prosecutor said that it was likely that Kevin would die from his injuries, although at that time he was being kept alive by a life support machine.

I spotted Gaynor sitting at the back of the court to my right wringing her hands nervously as Marie's solicitor asked for bail. Bail was not granted and Marie was remanded in custody to Her Majesty's Prison at Risley near Warrington. Gaynor was distraught. She stood up and ran to the door and as she brushed past me I heard her muttering,

"It's my fault, it's my fault."

On the Thursday I was down at the police station to interview one of my clients who had stolen fifty recently planted conifers from a newly built bungalow on the outskirts of Rotherham. As I was waiting Gaynor walked into the station and I asked how her stepfather was.

"The last I heard," she said, "was that he was still very ill, but I've not heard anything for a couple of days."

"How is your mum?" I asked.

"She's OK. She's proved to be much stronger than I ever thought she would be. I see her every other day and she writes every day. She's been fantastic really. She's settled in and has told me that the other prisoners have a lot of respect for her because she stood up to a bully."

Gaynor sounded quite bright but there was no doubt that she was finding it very difficult to come to terms with her mother's predicament.

As I chatted to her I could not help noticing how quiet and withdrawn she was, but then two officers appeared at the doorway, one of whom was a detective inspector.

He spoke very formally.

"Gaynor Pearson, I have to inform you that there has been a development in the case of the wounding of your stepfather. I have to tell you that the good news is that he has regained consciousness and the hospital staff are confident he will make a full recovery, although it may be sometime before he will be fit enough to be released."

Gaynor breathed a sigh of relief, but then the officer spoke again.

"I now have to inform you that we have had the opportunity of interviewing Mr Kevin Kelly and we now have his account of what happened on the night in question. It is with that information therefore that I have to say to you Gaynor Pearson I arrest you on suspicion of attempting to murder Kevin Kelly on the 18th of this month. You are not obliged to say anything unless you wish to do so but whatever you say will be taken down and used in evidence."

I held my breath. Gaynor made no protest and simply bowed her head. All I heard her say was,

"It was all my fault."

Before she could be taken away I advised the police that I was Gaynor's solicitor. He turned to Gaynor and asked her a question.

"Is that true Miss Pearson, that you wish Mr Smith to be with you when you are interviewed?"

She nodded and said yes and we were led into the cell area.

Chapter Twelve

THE SINS OF THE MOTHER

I had completely forgotten about my friend with the conifers as Gaynor was taken to the charge office and booked in. She was then placed in a cell.

The detective inspector took me to one side to explain what had happened in the case.

"To be perfectly frank with you, we were always a bit suspicious about this case so we decided to leave our enquiries until the man regained consciousness. Fortunately for him, he did so." said the inspector gravely.

"He told us that he came home and found Gaynor on her own. He asked her what she was doing in the house and she gave him a mouthful. There was a very violent argument and she stabbed him. It was as simple as that."

I didn't think it was as simple as that. There was something about this case that did not make any sense.

"I think there's more to this than meets the eye," I said to the police officer, "But if you can give me ten minutes with Gaynor I'd like to speak to her before she is interviewed."

I went into the cell area, but as there was no interview room free I had to go into a cell. It was a small stark room with walls plastered in graffiti. A strong smell of bleach hung in the air and there was only a wooden bench to sit on.

Gaynor was brought in and she sat on the bench next to me.

I had considerable sympathy for this girl, but she was resigned to her fate. Something did not make sense.

I asked her to tell me the full story.

Gaynor's eyes narrowed as she began. She had been round to see her mother when she knew her stepfather would be out, but she arrived before her mother had got home and had been surprised when her stepfather returned home early. Primed with a mixture of drink and the desire to dominate the stepdaughter he disliked so intensely Kevin had grabbed her and tried to impose himself upon her as she left the bathroom. Gaynor spurned his advances and tried to get him off. At this moment, Marie arrived and heard Gaynor's screams. She rushed upstairs and was horrified to see what was happening. Marie tried to interfere but Kevin thumped her in the face with two powerful punches. She fell to the floor and banged her head splitting it open at the back.

Knowing she didn't have the strength to physically stop what she feared was going to happen, Gaynor looked around for something to hit him with. The first things she saw were two pairs of scissors on the bathroom shelf. Gaynor then seized one pair and stabbed Kevin repeatedly in the back until he slumped to the floor.

The two women sat in silence as the enormity of what Gaynor had done gripped them both. They held each other for what seemed an eternity before Marie, took complete charge and telephoned the emergency services. The ambulance arrived together with the Rotherham police to find the two blood splattered women still huddled together by the telephone.

Kevin was taken to the hospital as he was seriously injured and close to death, having lost a substantial amount of blood.

Gaynor was also injured and in a considerable state of shock. Both her eyes were swollen and her nose was bleeding following the thunderous blows that Kevin had given her to stop her struggling. The police questioned Marie as the ambulancemen checked her injuries and she immediately volunteered a confession while Gaynor looked on unable to speak.

Both women were then taken to the hospital and after further checks Marie was taken to the police station where she was formally interviewed and she made a full admission as to what had taken place. She was charged with attempted murder and kept in custody until court the following day.

Marie had not instructed me to act in her defence as she had chosen to use the duty solicitor who was available during the early hours of the morning while I was fast asleep. She had then been taken to the prison at Risley in Warrington while her common-law husband fought for his life in the Rotherham District General Hospital.

Gaynor had also been detained in hospital as it was suspected that she was suffering from concussion and shock. She was not released until three days later during which time she had hardly spoken to anyone.

At this point Gaynor stopped speaking and looked straight at me. I had not interrupted her once during her account of what had happened and I now sat back on the bench surprised by the revelations.

"But you know you'll be charged with it now," I said.

"Not quite," said Gaynor, "You see I've decided that I'm not going to say anything to the police unless they promise to release mum and take no action against her. She was as upset as me you see, and didn't know what she was saying."

"I don't think the police can guarantee that," I said.

"Well," said Gaynor, "If they can't, I can't guarantee that I'm going to speak to them."

I was surprised at just how calculating Gaynor was. I had filled in a legal aid application and taken some notes but because there wasn't a desk in the cell, it was difficult to write.

Almost at the same time that Gaynor finished her story, a policewoman entered the cell to say that they were ready to interview her.

When I stood to leave I had forgotten that I had put my fountain pen on my lap and it fell towards the floor. With amazing speed Gaynor stretched out her left hand catching the pen before it hit the concrete floor.

"Hey, I'm most impressed. That was one of the quickest moves I've seen in a long time," I said trying to lighten the proceedings.

"I play a lot of badminton," said Gaynor, "And I think it's sharpened up my reactions."

"Not bad to say you're getting on a bit," I joked in my attempt to cheer her up as we were into the interview room.

The police had quite a degree of sympathy for the two women, but they stressed that they could not give Gaynor any guarantees about what would happen to her mother as it could be said that they would be offering some kind of inducement.

However, Gaynor was very open in the interview, taking care to absolve her mother completely from all liability. She claimed quite vociferously that she has had acted in self-defence, although it was certainly open to question if using a knife in that particular way amounted to self-defence.

After the interview, the police contacted The Crown Prosecution Service and arrangements were put in hand for Marie to be returned to court for the magistrates to reconsider bail.

Against all the odds, I was successful in my bail application for Gaynor, although the conditions imposed were extremely tough.

During the interview the police had been good enough to let me have copies of the medical statement, together with detailed photographs showing Kevin's injuries. My problem was how to confirm what really happened as there were now three versions of the incident.

By a strange coincidence, that very evening I attended a lecture at the Medico-Legal Centre in Sheffield and one of the speakers was a specialist in forensic medicine. He gave a very interesting talk about injuries and the way judgements can now be made as to how wounds had been inflicted by studying medical reports, detailed photographs and the weapons.

I still had Gaynor's papers in my briefcase as I wished to study them at home that evening, so during the coffee break I asked the expert questions about knife wounds which led us into a brief discussion about Gaynor's case.

I showed him the medical report and the photographs, from which he made a rather startling discovery.

He told me that out of the six wounds that had been sustained by Kevin, the photographs and the report confirmed that four had been inflicted by someone using their right hand and the remaining two by the left hand. He said that he thought at some stage during the attack, the assailant had switched the weapon from one hand to another, though he was unable to say at what stage.

As he spoke I could not help thinking back to seeing Marie in my office with her arthritic left hand, and Gaynor's reaction in the cells when I dropped my pen and she caught it with her left hand. A rather disturbing picture was beginning to form in my mind and so I questioned the expert further.

"Could another possible explanation be that the right-handed wounds were inflicted by one person and the left-handed wounds by another?" I asked.

"Of course it could," he said, "That would certainly be another possibility."

I was reflecting upon what he said when another eager questioner distracted his attention. I thanked him and went to claim my free coffee and biscuits.

The following day was a Saturday and I had to attend the morning court for three prisoners. One of the cases involved a persistent shoplifter with whom the police had lost patience and they were asking the court to remand him in custody. The second was the town drunk, who'd been arrested for the fifth time that week, and the third was an unfortunate burglar who had broken into a scrap yard to steal 'a bit of stainless'. He had fallen foul of the owner's Rotweiller, who had chased him and bit him on his bottom as he had tried to clamber over a wall. He had been taken to the hospital for his wound to be dressed and to have a tetanus injection, and had spent a painful, sleepless night in the police station cells. In court that morning he was still in some considerable discomfort following Tyson's attack.

The list was finished by 11.00am, with the shoplifter free to carry on shoplifting, the town drunk to carry on drinking and the scrap yard burglar went home to rest on his laurels.

On the Monday the formalities of Gaynor's case were dealt with extremely quickly and a date before the end of the year was arranged for the trial at Sheffield. Owing to the different stories which Marie and Gaynor had given to the police, separate Counsel had to be instructed for each defendant. It was indeed a bizarre case.

I was used to dealing with two defendants who blamed each other, but it was highly unusual to have two co-accused both blaming themselves and absolving each other.

The prosecution had a man seriously injured by knife wounds inflicted by one weapon. Someone had done it and it was a matter for the jury to decide who that person was but surprisingly, there was no forensic evidence. I believed that this was because Marie had admitted the charge immediately it had happened and the police would have thought that there wouldn't be any need to go to the expense of detailed

237

forensic testing. However it was only when Kevin regained consciousness that another version of the incident came to light. Kevin's evidence was not particularly reliable owing to his drunken condition at the time. His blood had been tested when he arrived at hospital and was found to be four times over the legal limit. He also admitted that he couldn't remember certain parts of the incident.

Gaynor claimed self-defence saying that Kevin had chosen to be selective so far as his memory was concerned and the part he couldn't recall was when he had launched his vicious attack on her.

As the defence of self-defence insists that a person is only entitled to use a proportionate amount of force to that which is being used against them, the jury had to decide three things before considering anything further.

Firstly they had to decide who inflicted the wounds: Secondly, whether it was fair to use a knife when the attacker was not so armed and finally if it was thought to be fair, whether the number of blows was excessive.

My argument was that firstly the prosecution had to prove beyond reasonable doubt who had caused the wounds. Secondly, Kevin was a big powerful man, over six feet in height and seventeen stones in weight. He had a history of violence and that night was drunk and dangerous. He had shown in the past that he had no control over his temper and therefore a weak and relatively speaking powerless woman would have to take extreme measures to defend herself against such a man. Thirdly if the jury accepted the last point, what number of blows can be seen as excessive if the defendant believed that there was a very realistic prospect of one or both of the women being killed?

I hoped for a sympathy vote from the jury but in a case such as this, anything could happen and in the event it did.

On the first day of the trial both Gaynor and Marie were terrified.   If they needed to learn any lesson from what they had done it had been learned during the waiting period leading up to the trial.   Marie was determined to take as much of the responsibility as possible for she said she had less to lose. However Gaynor wanted to protect her mother.   Therefore the result was a stalemate.

By the time of the trial Kevin had fully recovered despite the serious nature of his injuries.   Apart from one visit to the house with the police to collect his belongings there had been no contact between him and Marie and Gaynor since the incident but he suggested that they had not seen the last of him.

He had left the area and was living with a sister somewhere in the Manchester area.

By 10.45am he had not appeared at court and the prosecuting counsel asked the police to find him.   The case was adjourned until 12 noon for enquiries to be made.   At noon the case was put back until 2.00pm.

At 2.00pm we were told that Kevin was well aware of the hearing but had chosen to take a day trip to Calais to bring back some duty free booze for his forthcoming wedding celebrations He had deliberately avoided telling the police so that Marie and Gaynor would have to suffer the long wait at court and the uncertainty of their futures.

Kevin had not endeared himself to the prosecuting authority or to anyone else for that matter.   My opposite number at the Crown Prosecution Service told me that there were warrants outstanding for his arrest for non-payment of fines and a little matter of failing to appear at the Manchester Magistrates Court for police assault.

"It seems that the complainant has skipped the country and will not be returning in the foreseeable future," said my colleague.

"Well it looks to me as though you are up the creek without a paddle," I suggested with tongue firmly in cheek. "How are you going to prove your case now? There's nothing to counter what the defendants have said."

"But how do you explain the wounds?" he asked.

"No," I replied firmly, "How do you explain them? In any event what does it matter, he's a rotten shit anyway!"

"Is that what we have to tell the judge?" asked my colleague.

"Why not," I replied, "You can leave out the word rotten."

He laughed and went to discuss the situation with his Counsel. If we had been talking about a black eye or a broken nose I suppose there wouldn't have been much difficulty, but as we were dealing with serious injuries it remained to be seen if the Judge would sanction a dismissal of the charges.

I went in search of Gaynor and Marie and found them downstairs just outside the tea room. I persuaded them to have some tea but they declined the offer of a bacon sandwich and some toast which I had brought with the tea. Waste not, want not, I thought and tucked into the bacon sandwich.

During my feasting I noticed a marked silence between mother and daughter. I did not expect them to be particularly talkative, but there was something else which I could sense. It became obvious that they were waiting for me to finish and as soon as I had, I questioned them. "Apart from being here, is there something which is troubling you?" I asked.

At first there was no reply at first but then Marie spoke.

"There's something we need to tell you," announced Marie, "It's about our case, we think we should tell.............."

Just then we were interrupted by our Counsel who required an urgent word.

I made my apologies to Marie and walked off to an interview room close by. The news our Counsel gave me was a massive relief, but I had done this job for too long to pass on such information until it was confirmed. There is nothing worse than building up hopes only to dash them later.

While I was waiting for our Counsel to return from seeing the judge I waited in the body of the court avoiding Marie and Gaynor and the earth shattering news they wanted to impart.

Within five minutes both Counsel for the defence and the prosecutor returned from the judge's chambers. The thumbs-up sign meant that the prosecution had decided albeit reluctantly not to proceed with the charge due to all the surrounding factors. However, the matter would 'lie on the file' not to be proceeded with without the leave of the court.

While neither Marie nor Gaynor had been acquitted by the jury and could not lay claim to a not guilty verdict, it was good enough. There was also no conclusion for opposing Counsels but there was honour on both sides.

My colleague from the Crown Prosecution Service approached me and said,

"It wasn't really worth bothering with. It seems that the complainant had been told that he wouldn't be able to claim criminal injuries compensation and so he had thought 'sod it'. However he decided to ensure your clients would have to be put through the mill first. The judge took a pragmatic view and said he would not object to the course suggested which in short means that he thought our complainant was in all probability a rotten shit!"

I didn't answer but I think the grin gave me away.

I set off to see Gaynor before anyone else could. She was sitting in the tea room holding hands with her mother   I couldn't help feeling sorry for them but this time there was going to be no kick in the teeth.

"Gaynor, can I have a quick word? Marie, your solicitor will be coming in a moment but he doesn't mind if I tell you…….."

"Steve," said Marie solemnly, "It was…………"

Just then the investigating detective inspector walked passed us. As he did I interrupted Marie in return.

"It was three bacon sandwiches and tea I think you were going to say, is that right?" I said as I ushered them both into the tea room.

"But……" protested Marie.

When the officer was out of earshot I blurted out the news. Both ladies hugged each other and then me and then the tears came.

I left them alone in a quiet part of the tea room while I ordered the sandwiches.

"Are these all for you?" asked the lady canteen assistant in a gruff man's voice with a smoker's cough.

"Probably!" I replied as I looked back at two very relieved ladies. "Yes, probably……" I continued.

The canteen lady mumbled something under her breath but I wasn't listening.

"I said rind on or off?" said the assistant forcefully.

"Er…off please," I said thoughtfully.

"Fried or grilled?" was the next question.

"Er……fried please."

"Brown or white?"

"Er……white please, yes white will be fine."

"Drink?"

"Er……yes please."

"Which?"

"Er……..tea I think, yes tea - make that three."

"Three teas?" she replied as if she believed they were all for me.

"Black or white?"

"Oh bloody hell" I thought to myself.

"Three white teas, one with sugar, two without, cups not mugs, one spoon, small."

"Er........." she thought to herself for a moment as I smiled thinking I had got one over on her, but a second later,

"One lump or two?"

We both smiled.

"Two please madam, thank you." I said.

"Certainly Sir," came the reply and off she went to her frying pan.

I delivered the tea and sandwiches. The tea was taken readily and this time, much to my disappointment so were the sandwiches.

As I sat down Gaynor reached for my hand, squeezed it and just said, "Thank you."

"Yes," I said, they are bloody good sandwiches aren't they......you are not going to eat all of them are you?"

Both mother and daughter laughed thinking I was joking. I laughed knowing that I was not.

Just then my old friend Terry Nunns from the Crown Prosecution Service arrived and invited me out to lunch. I could not miss that opportunity so I agreed to meet him in the grill next door. Marie and Gaynor were anxious to leave but I had to know what information they were going to give me earlier.

I asked Marie but before she could speak Gaynor chipped in.

"We wanted to know if you wanted a bacon sandwich."

"Oh," I said regretfully, "I thought it might have been something else."

"Well as a matter of interest," said Marie shrugging off Gaynor's reluctance, "We wanted to tell you who actually did..........."

Just then Peter Baker QC appeared and told me he wanted to speak to me about a case.

Gaynor seized the opportunity, took her mother's arm, said farewell and left, leaving me to be treated to two bacon sandwiches by my learned colleague. We discussed our case and Mr Baker left me to pay for the sandwiches.

I then went to meet Terry for lunch.

"They only had sandwiches, is that OK?" asked Terry.

"Fine," I replied. "Bur I have got to admit I have already had…."

At that moment three bacon sandwiches appeared…………I continued my conversation, "bacon sandwiches," I said.

"Your favourites I think," said Terry thinking he had done me a considerable favour.

"Yes, yes of course," I said beginning to eat.

"There's only one problem," said Terry.

"Go on," I replied expectantly.

"I've come out without any change."

I just nodded almost knowingly, but it had been a good day.

After lunch, I returned to the court and collected my things and on the way out I bumped into Gordon Trousdale, a court clerk and a good friend.

"Good result Smithy?" he queried.

"Certainly was," I answered hoping he was referring to the case.

"Fancy a quick bacon sandwich?" he continued.

"Just had seven," I replied.

"Good old Smithy," said Gordon, "Ever the wag. Seven bacon sandwiches?" Gordon laughed and walked off laughing.

As I drove back to Rotherham, I couldn't help wondering who had done what, but then did it really matter in the great scheme of things?……Yes it bloody did! Someday I would find out. Maybe when the dust has settled, I thought, maybe then, but it was one of those things you had to know. However, it was a satisfactory end to an unsatisfactory case. One thing was clear though, Kevin hadn't done it himself...........had he???

Chapter 13

BYE BYE ALBERT, JACK, MADGE, MORRIS, BORIS CLORIS & VENN ETC. ETC.

With only a week to go before Christmas, I realised that it was the day the Heptonstalls were moving north.

So I decided that I would pay one last visit to Jack's house to wave them off and wish them well as I had promised to do. When I arrived at the house there was all manner of transport waiting to carry Jack and his brood away to Northumberland. Jack and Morris had their Transit vans but there were other vehicles driven by some rather curious people who I had not seen before.

With all the traffic, I had to park a little way down the street but walked up to the house just in time to see Albert's menagerie carried on to an extremely large removal van which had the words 'Ray's Removals' painted, rather less than professionally, on the side. I stood by the gateway and watched three dogs, two cats, seventeen racing pigeons and a large pig carried on board.

The next person to emerge from the house was a rather burly man with a huge beer belly. He had what looked like a snake around his neck and his face was extremely red as he struggled down the garden path, finally disappearing into the van not to be seen again.

A long-haired youth followed, dressed in biker's leathers, with a steel ring through the side of his nose. He carried a gorilla's head and a rather limp blow-up doll. Next came someone with a full suit of armour and a mounted moose head, complete with antlers. Jack then appeared with a large cardboard box full of cigars.

"Hey up Steve," said Jack, "It's reight decent of thee to turn 'art to see us afore we go."

"That's alright Jack, I've been into work and I was in the area so I thought I would just say hello, or rather goodbye."

I noticed that the whole street had turned out, almost as if it was some kind of party. Many of the neighbours had pitched in with carrying duties as the procession of the most unusual objects d'art appeared and then disappeared into the waiting vans.

"You have some very unusual antiques there Jack," I said.

"Aye," said Jack, "I've been collecting them for years 'tha knows. We were going to 'ave a shop but we never got round to it."

"Where's Albert?" I said.

"He's abart somewhere," said Jack, "He wants to see thee before 'e goes. We've got thee a present. It's a bit of a surprise really, but tha's been so good to me family over the years that we thought you might like something special to remember us by."

I couldn't help thinking that I had enough by which to remember this family. After all, I built my practice upon Jack's patronage, but it was a wonderful thought and a splendid gesture, and I could not help feeling deeply touched by their thoughtfulness.

As Jack and I were talking Madge appeared carrying a very heavy looking box.

"Can you manage that Madge?" said Jack

"Not really," said Madge, "It's a bit too heavy for me."

"Well do thee best then lass," said Jack turning to continue our conversation.

I was moved to try to help her, but she refused my offer saying that I would get my suit 'mucky'.

247

"Aye she's a good strong lass our Madge," said Jack as he allowed her to struggle with the box on her own. "Of course as she's got older 'tha knows, she's not as fit as she wor, but she can still lift like a gud 'n."

I was aware that Madge was doing much more of the lifting than Jack, but then Jack always said that he liked to 'share it out a bit'.

I was invited into the house, which was empty apart from the carpets and a telephone on the floor in the corner.

"We're leaving 'em that phone," said Jack with consummate generosity.

"You're generous to a fault Jack," I said noting that the telephone belonged to Telecom.

"Do you know Steve," said Jack, "I was born in this 'ouse."

"Were you really Jack?" I said.

"Aye, and our Morris too, and our Venn."

"What about Albert? Where was he born?" I asked thinking of the local lunatic asylum.

"At the 'ospital our Albert was, Madge 'ad a bit of trouble with 'im."

"Get away," I said, accepting every word. "He's certainly run too true to form all his life hasn't he?"

"Aye," said Jack, "'e's a good lad. I don't have favourites tha' knows, but if I 'ad I think it would be 'im. I just wish 'e were 'appier about moving. E's a funny lad our Albert is," said Jack.

"Get away," I said, "Who would have thought it."

There was a hint of a smile on Jack's face as I knew he had understood what I was saying.

"I'll tell you one thing Jack," I continued, "There's nobody quite like Albert. He is a character and a half and I've got to say that I really like him."

"Yeh," said Jack, "Everybody does. There's no 'arm in 'im really tha' knows. 'E's a bit deep and keeps things to 'is sen', but 'is 'eart's int reight place. 'E's reight loyal and 'e'd do 'owt for thee."

"It's very nice of you to say so Jack," I said.

"Aye," said Jack, "An' rest on us would an' all."

I smiled. I did not wish to embarrass the man, and I did not wish to be embarrassed myself as I realised that it was quite a solemn occasion for Jack leaving the home he had lived in for all of his fifty years.

"I certainly hope it works out for you Jack, I really do."

"Well I'm going to go straight Steve," said Jack. "It's a job and I'm going to do it the best I can, and the lads will be reight too."

"I think you should Jack, there's nobody can work with pigeons quite like you."

"No, only our Albert. 'E's a genius with animals 'tha knows," noted Jack.

I smiled, but before I could reply I noticed that Jack was looking round his house for the last time. It was a big thing for him and he had confessed to me earlier that he had never been out of Rotherham for more than a few days.

We walked outside to find his brood were all in a line. I shook hands with them all one by one, ending with Madge.

"Where's Albert?" I asked.

"'E's just gone to pick summat up for thee, we've got thee a present for looking after us," and with that Albert appeared. The cheeky grin which more often than not inhabited his face was conspicuous by it's absence as he walked up to me to make a solemn presentation.

"Steve, 'tha's not like a solicitor," he said.

I didn't quite know which way to take that comment, whether it was a compliment or not but he continued.

"And tha's always treated us with respect. We've always looked at other solicitors and they've got them gold watches on chains in their waistcoats. We've noticed that you 'aven't got one of them like proper solicitors 'ave."

I was beginning to be ill at ease with Albert's tribute, but the little fellow was doing his best and he continued.

"We've got thee this," said Albert thrusting something into my hands.

"Every time 'tha looks at this tha'll think of us," said Albert.

All of a sudden I felt very humble and I realised that I had been very moved by Albert's little speech.

"It's engraved 'an all," said Albert "We'll part as mates," and he held out his hand for me to shake.

I looked to see if there was any chewing gum hiding in between his fingers which he was going to deposit upon me, for that was one of his favourite party tricks, but for once there was none. His hands were spotlessly clean and there was a fine parting in his hair where he'd used tap water to make it stay down.

"By the way Albert there was something I wanted to ask you before you went?"

"Aye, what's that?" said Albert.

"What's a zit?"

"Tha' what?" said Albert.

"A zit," I said, "It's the word you use sometimes to describe people you don't like. What is a zit?"

"Oh, tha' knows what a zit is, summat 'orrible. It's that sound a spot makes when you squeeze it and it burst."

"Oh, thank you Albert," I said, wishing I had never asked.

Before I could open the present Albert simply said,

"I've got to go now. If you're ever up in our neck of the woods tha' can come and stop in one of our caravans."

I found myself accepting his offer, such was the emotion which passed between us. I could hardly suppress the lump in my throat. I opened the box and found a Hunter watch with a chain rather like those that proper solicitors wear.

The wagon train moved off and I looked to see Albert waving from the back of the removal van.

I have to say that I was quite overcome that they should have taken their time, effort and money to buy a present just for me.

I opened up the watch to read the engraved dedication. Squinting at the backplate as the winter sun reflected on the shining case, I could just make out the inscription: 'To Frank for fifty years with British Rail.........!'"

"A..L..B..E..R..T." I shouted, but to no avail. The wagon train had disappeared over the brow of a hill taking Jack and Madge Heptonstall and the kids on the way to a new world. For Jack it was the world of legitimate work: something he had never known before. For the family, it was a new area to explore and settle in.

I stood for some time with a smile on my face. Little did I know that it wouldn't be long before I was to see them again but if I told you how it came about...........you'd never believe it...................!!

To be continued.........................

POSTSCRIPT

Having finished writing 'Hell is Not for Angels' in 1995, I asked my publisher if he would have a look at a series of anecdotes I had written about my life in criminal law. I had prepared these for speaking engagements I had done over the years and had been told they were quite amusing.

Alan told me that short stories don't sell, but if I was to turn them into a novel, it might just work. I took up the challenge and 'Boozers' began to take shape, with a fit, young, handsome and highly successful Steve Smith as the narrator and central character. When I showed Alan the first chapters, he told me that the key to success in writing is to write about what you know. He sent me away to think about this and to come back when I had more to show him.

This is when 'Boozers Ballcocks and Bail' was born with a fat, drunken, ugly and incompetent, and maybe even incontinent, Steve Smith as the narrator and central character.

Alan congratulated me on how well I had acted on his advice and assured me that the book would be a great success. We published in December 1996 and 'Boozers' was an immediate bestseller. Earlier this year I signed a contract with television producer Stuart Doughty of Carnival Films for an option to make a TV series based on the book. A number of TV appearances, radio interviews and masses of press coverage have helped to keep the book selling and a recent invitation to speak at the prestigious Yorkshire Post Literary Lunch has made 1997 a year to remember.

All this, as well as the many kind letters from people I have never met but who had read and enjoyed the book, inspired me to write 'Plonkers Plaintiffs and Pleas' which continues my story through 1983. It features many of the wonderful characters from 'Boozers' and one or two new ones I met along the way. I hope you have enjoyed reading it as much as I have enjoyed writing it.

Stephen Smith
Rotherham
October, 1997